# Light a

## A Scientific journey
## into the Spiritual World

Dr. Konstantin Korotkov

Part III co-authored with Dr. A.L. Kouznetsov
Translated from Russian by author

Edited by Leonid Tunik
Cover Design by Jaroslaw Kupsc

ISBN 0-9644311-5-7
US$12.95

Distributed to the trade by ACCESS Publishers Network, 1-800-345-0096
Also available through Ingram, Baker & Taylor and other fine wholesalers

For information write to: Backbone Publishing Company
PO Box 562, Fair Lawn, NJ 07410, USA.
E-mail to info@bpc-us.com

Printed in the United States of America

# Part I · Death Does Not Exist

# Part II · Observations

# Part III · Morphogenetic Synergization of Biological Objects

# Preface

Our first set of observations was performed in 1993. Since that time our results were widely discussed in journals and newspapers published both in Russia and in Europe. In 1994, my book *Light after Life* was published in St. Petersburg (2$^{nd}$ edition in 1996). At large congresses in Russia, Germany, Finland and Shri-Lanka; at seminars in Italy, Sweden, Denmark and Australia the results of our study were the subject of long and fruitful discussions with scientists of many different specializations: physics, biology and medicine, including some leading pathologists. At all times we encountered interested and attentive response. The general opinion was that the study has launched a new stage in the investigation of the deepest, most basic questions of our existence, taking the next step in bringing together ancient esoteric perceptions and modern science.

Data discussed in this book were repeatedly reproduced both by us and by other explorers. The main results and conclusions were confirmed. The item of continuation and development of the study of post-mortal states, as well as the process of transfer from life to death itself comes to the agenda.

At the same time, all these years brought some new achievements. First of all, the hardware was immensely enhanced: a totally new generator for visualization has been developed, giving us better stability, repeatability and convenience in observational setup. The same equipment, now manufactured in larger numbers, is used in many research centers in various countries. On this basis, a device for computer registration of integral high-frequency currents has been developed, making it possible to study the dynamics of changes in energy-information state of an organism. The equipment for direct input of Kirlian images into computer, based on fiber-glass optics and TV elements, is also in a manufacturing stage now. This instrument opens up a new page in the history of bio-electrography: it enables the images to be registered in broad daylight and be processed in real-time with all the might of modern computer technology. A special elaborate software has been developed too, helping build up a system for diagnostics of energy-information state of a person and monitoring its responses to different influences, treatment, meditation and extra-sensory ability testing. All that enabled us to get some new interesting results, some of which have been published before [Korotkov 1995, 1996].

In this English edition we preserved the main bulk of the materials of the Russian edition, but revised it greatly and added a new section. As the result we produced a new book, with a much wider scope and a different title.

The composition of the book is as follows. The first part of the book begins with a brief review of historical, religious and occult ideas of the life of the soul after death. This review does not attempt to be exhaustive: in recent years, many works devoted to this subject became available worldwide, covering the question of death from different points of view. Our intention was to reveal the common thread relevant to the first 2-3 days after death. Special attention is devoted to the discussion of the ideas of the Orthodox Church as the original Russian faith, albeit suppressed through the decades of Communism. For us, citizens of the country of Orthodox Christianity, these discussion have a special value. The following chapter presents a discussion of the results received and the analysis of possible objections and errors, without technical details or technique description. Later in the book we present our personal interpretation of this data: our flight of imagination, night-time experiences, extra-sensory communication, etc. An unusual subject demands an unusual approach. The individual character of the material demanded to include the personal opinion of the author on the matter of life and death. For me, this subject has been the crux of deep reflections prompted by the dangerous games and encounters with death during my many years of mountaineering experience.

The next part of the book should interest scientists — the material offers an opportunity to evaluate both the course of the study and the chain of reasoning, and, if necessary, to reproduce this data.

This "rigorous" part of the book includes generalized information on physical/chemical changes occurring in the body during several days after death. It is now the domain of a specific science, Thanatology. The following chapters deal with the Kirlian effect technique and its application in observations, as well as with the principles of organization of the research. A separate chapter is devoted to the detailed analysis of observational data, with a description of each observation, its conditions and features. I should note that the observational technique was designed so as to account, to the extent possible, for the influence of all external factors and to avoid the influence of the observer. This principle was applied both to the observational technique and to the processing of results, performed on a computer using custom-developed software. In particular, special attention was given to the probable influence of atmospheric conditions, prompting us to include detailed data on the meteorological and electromagnetic atmospheric conditions at the time of the observations. The last chapter of this part is devoted to the discussion of observational data.

The third part of the book, written together with Dr. A. Kouznetsov, presents our ideas on connections between eastern philosophical ideas and western scientific approach. This is an attempt to use some contemporary physical ideas for the description of human organism, and, in principle, not only human, but rather a wide class of biological objects. It is very encouraging that we are no longer alone in these attempts: more and more scientists from different countries try to find their way to a new understanding of reality.

The material presented in this book is only an initial step toward a new and unknown area. Therefore the main purpose of our work has been to present an observational technique, our ideas associated with the preparation, organization, and observation itself as well as to discuss the data from all possible points of view. We hope that readers of all backgrounds will find this material interesting. We will be satisfied if the data presented here raises a discussion and results in new observations.

I would like to express my gratitude to all those who helped me in preparation and conducting of these observations, and especially to Helge Savolainen, whose moral and financial support was seminal in helping to start all this work.

This book has benefited directly and indirectly from various discussions and arguments with friends and colleagues: Professors Anatoly Akimov, Marco Bischof, Olga Burmistrova, Norbert Bankovsky, Gennady Dulnev, Antony J. Perry, Roger Taylor, Vladimir Volchenko. Dr. Alexander Kouznetsov was very attentive to my ideas throughout all my work, and at a later stage has become not only a friend, but a co-author of part 3 of this book.

I am grateful to long conversations with spiritually gifted people such as Leonid Astachov, Allan Chumak, Aleksey Nikitin, Eduard Naumov, Victoria Rjabuchina, Dinara and Sam Slonimsky, Sergey Tereskin, who helped me understand the beauty and depth of subtle world.

I offer my special appreciation and respect to my dear friend and colleague Vagif Soultanov, brilliant doctor and scientist, mutual work and long conversations with whom cleared for me many ideas and notions.

I would like to thank my publisher Leonid Tunik for his help in preparing the English version of the text and his patience in accepting endless corrections and amendments.

The writing of this book would have been impossible without the help and support from my wife, Svetlana, and I am deeply thankful to her for her unfailing inspiration and encouragements.

# Part I

# Death Does Not Exist

*Wherever I be born, there and then,*
*Let it come that I meet the Conquerors,*
*The peaceful and the wrathful deities;*
*Being able to walk and to talk as soon as [I am] born,*
*Let it come that I obtain the non-forgetting intellect*
*And remember my past life.*

*"The Tibetan Book of the Dead"*

# Prologue

Is there life after death? This question has been around for ages. It does not rise and fall with current fashions and big advertising campaigns. From time immemorial—ever since our species evolved into thinking creatures worthy of the name Homo Sapiens—this problem has been of the most basic and common concern. In studying the customs, rites and beliefs of primitive cultures the anthropologist always finds detailed constructions of the underworld, the place of departed spirits of the dead. Magicians and shamans, wizards and sorcerers, our liaisons with the intangible, are supposed to be able to travel to the underworld regularly so as to come into contact with the deities and the ancestors' spirits.

## The soul in afterlife—beliefs in ancient cultures

Ancients saw a multitude of deities and creatures taking care of the spirits in the underworld. two opposites were emphasized in most religions. They were light and darkness, reward and punishment, paradise and purgatory.

Ancient Egyptians worshipped Osiris as the god of the dead, placing him at the top of the Egyptian pantheon. In the land of the dead, the Ialu Fields, Osiris warmly welcomed the souls of the just. As the god of the dead Osiris enjoyed great popularity among the living, for he gave his devotees the hope of an eternally happy life in another world ruled by a just and good king. Isis, in the Osirian myth, represents the rich plains of Egypt. One who dies is led into the judgment hall by Anubis who then weighs the dead man's heart while Amemait, the Devourer, looks on anxiously. Amemait, eternally hungry monster with the trunk of hippopotamus, paws of a lion, and the maw of a crocodile, was handed the guiltiest hearts. On the other hand, whenever a favorable judgment is rendered the deceased departs victorious. From then on, he will lead a life of eternal happiness in the kingdom of Osiris.

In Egyptian mythology, the human being consists of eight substances: Name, Body, Shadow (also the source of sexuality), Glow, Living Force, and Immortal Part of the Soul *Bah*. The person dies when Bah, a falcon with a human head, leaves the deceased's body through the mouth. A person is reincarnated when Bah returns to the mummy. This was the very reason for mummification: to preserve the body for the return of Bah [Rahk, 1993]

In Assyrian-Babylonian mythology, queen Ereshkigal, also called the Star of Lamentation, and king Nergal were the rulers of the underworld.

Among other infernal deities we meet the divinities of Aztecs who believed in an upper world where the heavenly powers reside, a low world of the dead, and a central world lived in by men and spirits. The underworld was ruled by the infernal deities; Mictlantecuhtli and his wife Mictanchihuatl governed the nine underground rivers and the souls of the dead.

In Indian mythology, the judge of men and king of the invisible world was Yama—the guide to everyone who ventures into the next world. In his kingdom, friend is restored to friend, wife to husband, child to parents, and all become tranquil, since they are relieved of the ills of earthly existence. Upon death, one's sight rises up to the sun, breath to the wind, speech to the fire, blood to the water. Having left the shell of flesh, the soul lingers for a while, until it is carried away by the Wheel of Transmigration.

Chinese mythology allows the soul a much shorter life. Kuei, the vital force, joins the earth immediately upon death, and Shen, the essential personal element, stays for a longer time, but then disintegrates as well.

*The Tibetan Book of the Dead* deserves a more detailed treatment because it is a fairly complete account of the eastern view on post-mortal existence. *The Tibetan Book of the Dead,* or Bardo *Thödol is* a sacred book of litanies to be recited by the lama *over* the body of the deceased for 49 days after death with the intention of helping the soul of the deceased overcome the difficulties of afterlife existence and seeing it through either to Nirvana or to the next incarnation. *Bardo Thödol* literally means "Liberation by Hearing on the After-Death Plane", and implies *yogic* method of coming forth into *Nirvanic* Liberation, beyond the Cycle of Birth and Death. Less literally, the Book contains instructions for the living, teaching them to be prepared for the inevitable exit from this world. The instructions help us with the transfer of conscience so as to free the flux of life from the burden of the dying body, thus reaching fullest possible consciousness after death, to be in the state of awareness when we face the original Light and step onto the Great Rising Road leading to the Dharma-Kai of non-birth, or at least to a favorable succeeding re-birth.

*"To be born as a human being is a privilege, according to Buddha's teachings, because it offers the rare opportunity of liberation through one's own decisive effort, through a "turning about in the deepest seat of consciousness". If the disciple has learned, as the Bardo Thödol directs, to identify him or herself with the Eternal, the Dharma, the Imperishable Light of Buddhahood within, the*

*fears of death will be dissolved like a cloud of mist before the rising sun. Then the disciple knows that whatever he may see, hear, or feel, in the hour of his departure from this life, is but a reflection of his own conscious and subconscious mental content; and no mind-created illusion can then wield power over him if he knows its origin and is able to recognize it. The illusory Bardo visions vary, in keeping with the religious or cultural tradition in which the percipient has grown up, but their underlying motive-power is the same in all human beings. Thus it is that the profound psychology set forth by the Bardo Thödol constitutes an important contribution to our knowledge of the human mind and the path that leads beyond it. Under the guise of a science of death, Bardo Thödol reveals the secret of life; and therein lies its spiritual value and its universal appeal." (Govinda, 1960).*

The text falls into three parts. The first part, called *Chikhai Bardo,* is a description of the phenomena taking place in the mind at the time of dying. The second part, or *Chönyid Bardo,* describes the dream-like state immediately following the arrival of death and consisting of '*karmic* illusions'. The third part, or *Sidpa Bardo,* deals with incarnation, beginning with the instinct for rebirth and describing the events preceding the reincarnation, or rebirth. Apart from the three *Bardo* of death, the manuscript covers the three *Bardos* of life. Bardo of the Belly, when we are carried in our mother's womb; Bardo of Sleep, when experiencing a recollection of oneself in one's dreams; and Bardo of Mystic Enlightenment, when, in the waking state we forgets ourselves without losing consciousness.

Brilliant mystic images represented in the Book of the Dead are deeply laden with psychological wisdom of the soul's perception of our karmic essence as human beings. This thought was brilliantly expressed by Carl Gustav Jung (1875-1961) in his remarkable commentary on the *Tibetan Book of the Dead* (Jung, 1960).

*"...the Bardo Thödol offers one an intelligible philosophy addressed to human beings rather than to gods or primitive savages. Its philosophy contains the quintessence of Buddhist psychological criticism; and, as such, one can truly say that it is of an unexampled superiority. Not only the 'wrathful' but also the 'peaceful' deities are conceived as sangsãric projections of the human psyche, an idea that seems all too obvious to the enlightened European, because it reminds him of his own banal simplifications...*

*Metaphysical assertions, however, are statements of the psyche, and therefore psychological...*

*It is the soul which, by the divine creative power inherent in it, makes the metaphysical assertion; it posits the distinctions between metaphysical entities. Not only is it the condition of all metaphysical reality, it is that reality..*

> "*O nobly-born (so and so), listen. Now thou art experiencing the Radiance of the Clear Light of Pure Reality. Recognize it. O nobly-born, thy present intellect, in real nature void, not formed into anything as regards characteristics or color, naturally void, is the very Reality, the All-Good.*
>
> *Thine own intellect, which is now voidness, yet not to be regarded as of the voidness of nothingness, but as being the intellect itself, unobstructed, shining, thrilling, and blissful, is the very consciousness, the All-good Buddha.'*
>
> *...The fullness of its discriminative manifestations still lies latent in the soul."*

*The text continues:*

> '*Thine own consciousness, shining, void, and inseparable from the Great Body of Radiance, hath no birth, nor death, and is the Immutable Light—Buddha Amitbha.'*
>
> *The soul (or, as here, one's own consciousness) is assuredly not small, but the radiant Godhead itself. The West finds this statement either very dangerous, if not downright blasphemous, or else accepts it unthinkingly and then suffers from a theosophical inflation. Somehow we always have a wrong attitude to these things. But if we can master ourselves far enough to refrain from our chief error of always wanting to do something with things and put them to practical use, we may perhaps succeed in learning an important lesson from these teaching, or at least in appreciating the greatness of the Bardo Thödol, which vouchsafes to the dead man the ultimate and highest truth, that even the gods are the radiance and reflection of our own souls..." (Jung, 1960).*

The above passages illustrate one aspect of the sacred book, an aspect of great importance in the context of the present discussion, because it is characteristic of the Oriental approach to the understanding of human soul.

In other sacred books, such as the *Egyptian Book of the Dead*, similar approaches can be found, though often without a profound philosophical analysis. The Egyptian Book of the Dead relates to us the wanderings of the soul pending judgment by Osiris. Egyptians use the same principle to recognize the divine essence upon encounter with a Deity in the infernal kingdom. Both books state the necessity to integrate with the One you see through your mind's eye. The difference is that in the Tibetan book, the Sign

(Deity) appears first and must be recognized in order to become it. In the Egyptian book, the Soul must first become a Deity (a Sign) from the very start to avoid being extinguished. Entry into the Kingdom of Osiris and presentment to the sovereign judge is otherwise impossible.

Thus, from the point of view of the Eastern eschatology[1], the ultimate creator of the world's fate is the individual, whose rebirths and existence in both worlds, depend entirely upon his actions, thoughts and decisions, and upon his karma, which is the product of a person's actions during the successive phases of existence. The ultimate creator of his own circumstance, the individual makes or breaks each possibility. This point of view parallels the Christian doctrine, which teaches that the soul's afterlife depends upon the manner of the individual's earthly life, which is essential in the context of the results we have obtained.

Finally, the Great Religions—Brahmanism, Buddhism, Judaism, Christianity, and Islam, which have spread across frontiers, races, or languages—are the quintessence of all ancient beliefs. They all tell of existence after earthly life, though they tell different tales.

> "Christianity, in its orthodox form, rejects the most ancient and widespread belief of the Küklos genesen, or Sansāra, or 'Reincarnation', and admits one universe only—this, the first and the last—and two lives, one here in the natural body and one hereafter in the body of Resurrection...
>
> The need of some body always exists, except for the non-dualist who believes in a bodiless (Videha) Liberation (Mukti); and each of the religions affirms that there is a subtle and death-surviving element—vital and physical—in the physical body of flesh and blood, whether it be a permanent entity or Self, such as the Brahmanic Ātmā, the Moslem Ruh, and the Christian 'Soul', or whether it be only a complex of activities (or Skandha), psychical and physical, with life as their function—a complex of continual change, and, therefore, a series of psychical and physical momentary states, successively generated the one from the other, a continuous transformation, as the Buddhist are said to hold. Thus to none of these Faiths is death an absolute ending, but to all it is only the separation of the Psyche from the gross body. The former then enters on a new life, whilst the latter, having lost its principle of animation, decays." (Woodroffe, 1960).

To conclude—we see the same concept recurring in various and opposite parts of the globe, at different times, dressed up in distinct ornaments and bearing a multitude of names. It is the concept of the soul, which inspirits

---

1   *the branch of theology concerned with death, resurrection and immortality*

and elevates *Homo Sapiens* above the feral world and assigns it a special role in the Universe. It is the soul that provides a form of existence after earthly life, when the flesh is no more.

The materialist view on the idea of the soul as a single concept inherited from one of the ancient cultures by each new civilization does not hold up to serious criticism. One may have some success in finding Assyro-Babylonian roots in the ideas of ancient Judaism, but it would be absurd to look for an absolute common denominator between the various beliefs developed in the East Mediterranean, India, China, Americas and elsewhere. Even assuming the existence of a common base for all these cultures, inherited from an ancient civilization lost in time [Hancock, 1995], we should acknowledge the fact that only those ideas impregnate the spiritual life which are natural and coherent with it. It seems much wiser to concede that all ideas of the soul have originated independently—by means of comprehension through meditation, as well as through mystic contacts of outstanding thinkers from various nations with the Supreme Universal Mind.

> *"Thinkers of all denominations have always been concerned with the soul. The Hades and Tartarus, the mystic rites and ceremonies, the judgment by Osiris, the Inferno, Purgatorio and Paradiso in Dante's Divine Comedy, the revelations of Zen, the secrets of the Tibetan Book of the Dead, the apocalyptic pictures in the Bible of the end of the world described by the Christian prophets, the elaborate numerological symbolism of Kabbalah, the Jewish mystical philosophy, the no less elaborate symbolism of modern numerology, the doctrines and beliefs of modern theosophy, the definitions of psychotronics... The Adventist prophecies and the Shiism of the fanatical imams, the esoteric mystery cults and the belief in glossolalia, the witchcraft and astrology. Religious theories: historical, anthropological, culturological, phenomenological, psychological, cosmological."* (Tokarchik, 1992).

Below is a brief review of contemporary European ideas on the life of spirit after death. The problem is of importance for a better understanding of the context of this work and interpretation of its results of the research. In the recent few decades, tomes have been written on the subject. Our aim in this section is to leaf through some of the more relevant writings consistent with our views.

# Spiritual life after death according to the Bible.

The Gospel has been guiding the lives of about half the humankind for nearly two thousand years. The idea of eternal life spoken of by Jesus Christ has been written by the Apostles, who have conveyed one and the same meaning in different words. Christians believe in the Last Judgment. Everything comes from God, and everything returns to God.

> *"I am Alpha and Omega, the beginning and the end, the first and the last"* (Rev. of St. John, 22, 13)
> *"God is love"* (John 1, 4:8)

The Gospel of John is a book of great religious ideas—Revelation, Incarnation, Regeneration, Communication of Life. God in His love sent Christ to save the world (John 3: 16-21), for God loved the world so much that He gave His only Son, so that they should all have eternal life. The Savior was sent to the world to suffer tortures and crucifixion so that mankind would be redeemed from vice by the saving grace of Jesus whose blood makes us free from sin.

> *"In the beginning the Word existed. The Word was with God, and the Word was divine... The Word became flesh and blood and lived for a while among us, abounding in blessing and truth, and we saw the honor God had given Him, such honor as an only Son receives from His father..."* (John, 1, 1-18).

When a Christian goes to the Holy Communion, it is with the thought, "Jesus and I are one." Death is redeeming from sins, payment for sins. On the other hand, the worst sin is but a drop in the sea of God's mercy and favors granted to the repentant sinner.

> *"God created the heaven and the earth... God created man in His own image, in the image of God created He him; male and female created he them."* (Gen. 1, 1-27).

God is for the living, not for the dead.

> *Now He is not God of the dead, but of the living; for all live to Him* (Luke, 20.38)

God is Light, Life, Love, Truth, Freedom. What God has created may not be destroyed, for He is the Most High. The idea of the Last Judgment's fire which must cure this place is noticeable throughout the Gospel.

Why are there pictures of Apocalypse? Why all this darkness that may reign, albeit temporarily, over light? If the Resurrection is there, then He was dead, was He not? Does it mean that everything is mortal?

It is not only the world that is perishable and mortal: every single being dies a death that is unlike the death of any other being. Everyone who comes into this world is guarded by two angels. The Guardian Angel of Life is watching over the individual from the right-hand side, protecting the person's life—because Death must not be allowed to arrive too early. On the left-hand side, the Angel of Death is watching over his or her death—because life must not last too long. There is also another, the Messenger Angel of many faces and of a thousand eyes. He watches the frail vein connecting the spirit with the body and unwaveringly severs it at a time known to him alone. Heavy slumber befalls the guardian angels, and when the rustle of the Messenger's wings awakes them, it is too late, all time is gone.

Only the human being can see the messenger and even have a premonition of his arrival. Frightened, the human implores to be granted more time, but to no avail: he is always overpowered. The Messenger is privy to the great secrets of existence—the Book of Life. Hard is the Messenger's lot, and great is his obedience. It may be that even he who wrote the Book of Life dreads to read it, since it is said to be more frightening than death. But how frightening is death?

God is in everything, and it has always been so, because Time does not exist for Him who is above eternity. It means that those who accept God and those who reject God make their own choices, and they choose life or death, respectively. The limit for those who avoid God, or reject him, is death. The finite limit is at the same time the beginning of infinity. Death is the final threshold, the very last turn, beyond which the fugitive expects freedom to do whatever is best for his or her own sake. Instead, the fugitive has to face the infinitude. Dreadful is the death of the fool who does not accept God, for God is life. Consequently, what we call death shall be our encounter with life. On the other hand, if we were really alive, there would have been no death. By accepting God, we choose life. By accepting death, we choose God.

> Whither shall I go from thy spirit?
>> Or whither shall I flee from thy presence?
> If I ascend to heaven, thou art there!
>> If I make my bed in shed, thou art there!
> If I take the wings of the morning
>> and dwell in the uttermost part of the sea,
> Even there thy hand shall lead me,
>> and thy right hand shall hold me.
>> *[Psalms, 139, 7-10]*

Jesus Christ is eternal life, and those who are with Him will be saved. Jesus is the resurrection and life. In this earthly life, everyone is subjected to the death of one's flesh, one's damaged substance. However, when the earthly life comes to an end in the form of death, the heavenly life begins, which does not lead to a "natural" death, and in which the spirit is the only substance. The spirit, or the soul, is the "inner human being" that is not perishable. The Life of the "inner human" may be taken away only by Him who had given it.

## Evolution of the concept of death in European history.

Gospel truths have been discussed and interpreted in Europe over many centuries. The public understanding of death and afterlife have evolved with the general social and psychological norms and mentality of the various social layers. Russian historian A. Gurevich writes:

> "Once the historian assumes a serious attitude toward death and enters into a serious study of the problem, it becomes readily apparent that death is not only a subject for demographic history, theology and the Church didactic. Death is one of the crucial parameters signifying the social conscience. Since the latter is never at a standstill in the course of history, the changes cannot help being manifested in the shift of Man's approach toward death. A study of the parameter may shed light on the humankind's attitude toward life with its primary moral values. Some scholars are of the opinion that an individual's attitude towards death may be regarded as an index signifying the type of civilization. One's perception of death exposes one's secret foundations. At the same time, the individual is the intermediate link between the cultural body and the social body, the two of which are unified through that very link. Hence, the perception of death and of the next world, of relations between the living and the dead represents a theme to be studied and discussed in order to improve the perception of many aspects of the socio-cultural realities of the past. The discussion may result in a proper assessment of the role of Man in history." (Gurevich, 1989).

So much has been written on the subject of death in history that it is virtually impossible to review all relevant works. For the major part, historians deal with the subject in the context of two thousand years of European history. Those were times when religious teachings dominated the public conscience, and the population of Europe concentrated their thoughts upon the ultimate things, such as death, judgment, reward in heaven, and punishment in hell. In the Middle Ages (1100-1500), there were a number of occasions, registered by historians, of widespread expectation of a near end of the world in different

European countries, not to mention a small number of adepts prophesying the same. During many a century, death was an essential component of culture. It was a kind of a screen that reflected all ethical values of medieval Europeans.

Detailed analysis of the evolution in the attitude toward death from the ancient ages until the present time can be found in the works of French historian Philippe Aries (1914-1984). Let us survey one of his books, the engaging and informative *Images of Man and Death* (Aries, 1985).

Aries' speculations were based on testimonial materials of different ages: pictures, drawings, monuments, tombstones. This is what he wrote about the location and role of the cemetery.

> *"In Rome and in Pompeii the dead were excluded from the town. The separation of the dead from the living is the most striking characteristic of these early images. The dead were not to trouble the living nor to mingle with them. All the same, they were neither banished to some faraway place nor altogether isolated: it was important that one could easily bring them placating offerings or eat and drink close to them. So they were deposited immediately outside the town, at its gates or along the roads leading to it. The tombs were situated on either side of the highway, constituting two narrow lines of graves stretching out across the countryside." (Aries, 1985)*

An alignment, then, rather than a space—nothing resembling our own cemetery. Coemetrium is a word that came later from the Greek into Christian Latin, and sepulcretum was rarely used. The concept of a special space reserved for burials did not exist: one buried the dead whenever one could, wherever one wanted to, provided it was outside the town.

As early as the first century, representations of death were evoking not so much the mysteries of the beyond as the delights of the present. The skeletons with the drinking vessels and mosaics in the triclinium were not supposed to be frightening; on the contrary, they were an invitation to pleasure, to make the most of life, whose brevity they called to mind: "Know yourself and your mortality"

As a result, the sacred side of death seemed diminished. Typical epitaphs, which, however, we should not take too literally, for they did not exclude other forms of worship of the dead or religions of salvation, all conveyed to the passerby the same disillusioned or even cynical message: "The hunt, the baths, games, and pleasure—that is life."

A change took place in the second and third centuries AD, one of the great periods of transformation in our cultural history. It was in the towns that the cemetery first made its appearance: behind the fine monument lining the road, humble tombs spread in a disorganized and random fashion over an irregular, bulging space.

> *"The medieval cemetery was quite different from a modern one. It was a public and sometimes noisy place with a few random tombstones and crosses, where people would come together, after attending mass, for instance. Like the church, with which it was now invariably associated, the cemetery (or the churchyard, as the cemetery was generally known in England), at the center of the public space, was a stronghold of social life. The Hellenistic and Roman space reserved for the dead and for those who brought them offerings, a space set apart from the dwellings of men, in the Middle Ages became a space common to both the living and the dead, where the presence of the dead eventually, although not deliberately, became quite discreet. This promiscuity of living and dead was characteristic of societies of the Western Latin world... The cemetery was also a resting place for the old, a playground for children, and a meeting place for lovers." (Aries, 1985)*

This contemplation let Aries to draw significant conclusions concerning attitudes of different ages and nations toward death and the dead. He defined some of the stages of these attitudes and followed their change through time. He began with early Christianity.

*"Universa fraternitas"*

*The dominant theme is that of waiting, repose, or sleep, just as it appears first in the language of epitaphs and, later, in the attitude of the recumbent figures. This period of waiting was rejected by learned theologians for the last time in 1334, but the memory of it survived not only in the dispositions of recumbent figures but in other documents of the twelfth and thirteenth centuries.*

*The damned are not presented (in the pictures). They certainly exist—Saint Matthew, among many others, mentioned them; but at first their presence is very discreet, or has been effaced. They are excluded from the field of the image just as they are from the memory of men and of God. Only the elect remain, not as individuals, but as a composite mass, there being no need for particular judgments to distinguish among them. It is enough that they belong to the body of the saints. All that lives on in each being enters en masse into the Kingdom. The individual is absorbed into the immense family of Adam, redeemed and saved.*

*We have thus arrived at an idea of the beyond which combines a cosmic expansion of heaven with a gathering of the human race: the universa fraternitas.*

*Beginning in the thirteenth century, this collective and massive conception of the world gave way to another representation, this time stemming from Matthew 25, in which the individual, in place of the species as a whole, became the center of the drama.*

*In making this transition from the Second Coming to the Last Judgment, we have passed from the general view of man as a species—the family of Adam and Eve—to an inventory in which each individual soul is an object of examination and the entire life is taken into account.*

*...it acquires a new element of pathos: death is the moment when each man intuitively recognizes his entire life, which is illuminated suddenly, as if by a flash of lightning, and is revealed to him in every detail.*

*The fact is that as early as the eleventh and twelfth centuries, something momentous happened which quite upset the topography of the beyond. It was the discovery of purgatory. Purgatory had certainly always existed in Christian thought. It was a place for errant souls that had managed to escape damnation but whose faults barred them from sharing the repose of the "saints". They suffered tortures that resembled those of hell, and they "returned" as ghosts to beg for the pity and prayers of the living.*

*I believe that the popularity of purgatory can be accounted for by two related phenomena. (XVII-XIX)*

*One is a change in its meaning: purgatory ceased to be a temporary hell, reserved for a few great sinners saved in extremes, and became the antechamber to heaven through which all the elect, with the exception of the canonized saints, had to pass.*

*The other is a change in sensibility which began to render intolerable the departure of loved ones. In the early stages of this development, corresponding to the wide diffusion of the idea of purgatory, it was the place where those who had passed away went and where, until one joined them, one communicated with them through prayer.*

*In the nineteenth century emerged an important phenomenon which, in its early stages, coincided with the success of purgatory. It became extremely tempting to see the beyond as a place for reunion, for re dis-*

*covering earthly affections, following the interval of trials between the death of spouses.*

*Closer relationships between the living and the dead also developed outside the churches, in positivist and even anticlerical milieu. This was a tide that swept the entire Western world, regardless of religious allegiances.*

*It produced two, only slightly different, attitudes. The first was that of the Catholics: they either brought purgatory closer to paradise, or else dispensed with purgatory altogether. For the dear departed, there was no longer a hell or a purgatory—only a home for tender earthly relationships reconstituted in eternity.*

*The second attitude was that of the non-believers, of whom there were many in the anticlerical milieu of the early nineteenth century. For them, what remained after death was not the soul posited by philosophers or Christians but a physical being, an astral body, which could even leave its impression upon a photographic plate when it responded to the appeals of the living.*

*In the end of nineteenth—beginning of twenties centuries—we are crossing a frontier and coming upon a new sensibility. Death has changed its place and its meaning. Violence, fear, and sexuality now invade a domain in which life and death have become inseparable. Death offers the opportunity for an otherwise impossible love affair. The theme is that of death and the young girl. The new element is eroticism—and in most cases violence, of which eroticism is but one aspect. The former master of ceremonies has become a hunter of humans.*

*In a world designed to deceive the eye, death is the secret of life; but it is a secret that hides nothing—nothing but nothingness. It is therefore not surprising that the spirituality of the period tended to see life as close to death." (Aries, 1985)*

All these changes strongly affected society's attitude toward death and lead to the modern perverse meanings.

*"Until the sixteenth and seventeenth centuries, and even much later among the working classes, death was confined by society to restricted areas or ghettos. In those days it was encountered only in churches, tombs, books of hours, and other such places.*
*With the sixteenth century came an important change whose effects are still being felt today. Death emerged from its lair, insinuating itself here and there in domains formerly proscribed to it. Gradually it came to be found everywhere.*

*Now a new alliance was forged between death, violence, suffering, and sex, one that was to affect the Western imagination.*

*Mystic ecstasy resembles a scene of death as much as a scene of love; the conjunction of death and desire gave rise to a new category of eroticism. The word was "morbid". It acquired a real aesthetic value, being understood as a variation of "the beautiful," and its effects was much sought after. Lovers were no longer content with one last embrace before death: now they desired to break through the wall and satisfy their desire with an exhumed corpse. Life was now impregnated with death.*

*Now daily life was never free of death, for death was everywhere present and cultivated. The fashion was not to fear it, but to live gladly in its presence.*

*Death was so ubiquitous in the nineteenth and early twentieth centuries because it represented both a real separation, which one appropriately mourned with tears testifying to one's stricken love, and also an appearance from which the residue of reality had to be expelled so that communications with the departed could be re-established.*

*Hence, the principal funerary customs of the period: exaggerated expressions of grief, cults of memory, and frequent visits to cemeteries and tombs.*

*Relegated to the secret, private space of the home or the anonymity of the hospital, death no longer makes any sign.*

*No mother, no wife, no children, no God: there appears now to be nothing at all in the wavering consciousness of the dying man.*

*The waters in which he is about to disappear are irresistibly reminiscent of the primordial ocean of the first days of the world and, at the same time, of the protective fluids of the womb. Death is associated with a return to birth, to origins. " (Aries, 1985)*

Now, when the world was made smaller by television, Internet, and air travel, the ways of thinking are being homogenized throughout the world, but every nation has its own habits, its own peculiarities. Let us look more close at the views of Russian Orthodox Church.

## Eastern Orthodox Church on afterlife

Reverend Archbishop Anthony writes about the life of the soul after leaving its robe of flesh,

*"When a Christian dies, his or her soul, which has been to a certain extent purified at exit from the body due to the fear of death—leaves the lifeless flesh. The soul is immortal. The soul continues to live the full life that was started on earth, and the soul retains all former virtues and vices. The afterlife of the soul is a natural continuation, and consequence, of life on earth. If the deceased was a pious Christian praying to God, if he or she had confidence in God, if one's best was done to obey His commandments, then the soul shall immediately perceive the joyful presence of God, and the soul shall partake in heavenly life, to a greater or smaller extent. If however the deceased was guilty of sacrilege and lived a sinful life on earth, then the soul shall feel anguish and eternal damnation. Pending the resurrection on the Judgment Day, the souls of the devout shall grow more joyous whereas the souls of the impious shall grow more miserable.*

*Maintaining life after the death of the body, the soul continues to possess the properties of personality and self conscience. The soul is able to feel, to be conscious, to perceive, to reason... It should be remembered, however, that outside the body the soul is not a complete individual. Wish as it would, the soul cannot change radically so as to be able to begin an entirely new life. The soul cannot lead a life that would be different from the one it used to live in earthly life. The soul cannot acquire any of the qualities it did not possess while it was in the human body on earth.*

*The above is the meaning of the words stating that there can be no repentance beyond the threshold of death. The afterlife of the soul goes along the same lines that the soul followed in earthly life."* (Anthony, 1953)

Another Archbishop also wrote about this problem. Archbishop Luka[1] was born in 1871 and lived all his life in Russia. An outstanding surgeon and scholar he was consecrated bishop in 1923. Ten days after the consecration he was arrested by Soviet authorities and spent the next twelve years in exile. During World War II his skills as a surgeon became invaluable and enabled him to resume his work at a hospital. He continued to work in the medical profession until he died in 1961. A recognized scholar, he was also a servant of the Church. Though his service to the Church brought him disfavor with Soviet authorities, his profound contributions to medicine outweighed that "handicap," and even brought him Stalin's Prize of the First Degree for a textbook on purulent

---

1    *his secular name was Professor Valentine Felixovich Voyno-Yasenetsky*

surgery. A profound thinker, Prof. Voyno-Yasenetsky writes on the subject of the afterlife of the soul:

> "There is a constant tie and interaction between the body and the spirit. Everything that comes to pass in the soul of an individual during his of her life is of importance and necessity for one reason—the reason that the life of the body and soul is closely connected with the spiritual life. It is in the spirit that all actions of the body and soul are reflected and kept forever. It is in the acts of body and soul that the spirit is formed. It is under the influence of body and soul that the spiritual life develops either towards good or towards evil. The life of the mind and the heart, as well as the miraculously coordinated function of all other organs, are needed while the spirit is being formed. Their function ceases as soon as the spirit becomes completed, or as soon as its direction has been defined. Eternal bliss of the righteous and eternal torments of the wicked should be interpreted in the sense that the immortal spirit of the former has received light and power after its liberation from the body and is free and unfettered to excel without limit toward good and God's love, whereas the dark spirit of the wicked, of the sinners and of the antagonists of God is to suffer eternal pangs of remorse and bitterness caused by their alienation from God and by the unbearable poison of wickedness and hatred. Human life is divided by death in two: the life of soul and body, and the life of soul and spirit." (Voyno-Yasenetsky, 1978)

This idea was further developed by Reverend Piotr Kalinovsky, who wrote:

> "There are people who believe that the afterlife is a uniform immobile state of eternal bliss or a similarly continuous and passive torment in hell. This is not quite so. The Christian doctrine teaches differently. Even in death, there can be no motionless dead stillness. By the time of corporeal death, the spiritual development of personality has not been concluded. In afterlife, the personality continues its development along the lines followed in earthly life. Life experience is completed only when the person's soul has learnt both parts of life—the earthly life and the afterlife. While staying in the body, the soul cannot perceive the spiritual world: the soul can only achieve it by means of spiritual life." (Kalinovsky, 1991)

The concept of spiritual life adopted by the Orthodox Church is important in principle, since it offers an opportunity for the believer to consider the end in peace and freedom, to await it with the peaceful submissiveness of the soul. The Archpriest Sergiy (Bulgakov) writes

*"Death is a supreme consecration, a revelation of the spiritual world. Even before they are dead, the dying can perceive the substances of spiritual world, the very heaven with Him who is above. The afterlife of an individual is not death, nor is it a dead faint of the soul, but is a continuation of life started on earth. Deprived of the body, the soul cannot take part in earthly life, but it can change and develop in spiritual life. It can get associated with the world of spirits, both light and dark, as well as with other souls. The afterlife is not a complete life, but the perception of God becomes apparent, as well as the perception of the true meaning of all acts and actions. In afterlife, God can be seen as clearly as the Sun can be seen in this life." (Bulgakov, 1935)*

The thoughts outlined above, as written down by the twentieth-century Orthodox Christian theologians, are all based on the millennial traditions of the Eastern Orthodox Church. "The Eternal Secrets of the Next World" published in Moscow in 1908 cited numerous incidents illustrating the righteous death experienced by the Orthodox saints and the holy fathers of the Church. Their souls are shown to be able to continue an active life in the next world, with examples of their contacts with the holy fathers of the Church.

*"Death of a body is like a natural transitory sleep that helps to restore, and renew, the spiritual and the corporeal powers. It may be compared to planting the seed in the earth. The seed must first perish—in order to enable the roots of a new life to grow firm and produce green plants bearing flowers and fruits in Eternity".(Vechnyia Zagrobnyia Tainy, 1908)*

The Orthodox Church teaches that the moment of death is always determined by the Lord, however accidental or untimely we may take it to be. The Archpriest Sergiy Bulgakov writes, "Corporeal (physical) death has for its arrival a time and a term that are internal". (Bulgakov, 1992) . This idea is supported and developed by another theologian who writes,

*"Death has internal causes for his arrival. The external factors such as an illness or an accident manifest themselves to take away the person's life, which occurs in all those cases when a further existence in the earthly world has become meaningless in terms of the individual's spiritual life. Birth and death are in the hands of Our Lord. The hour of death is often connected with the person's spiritual mission. The righteous often have a premonition of Death. They do not get frightened, often just awaiting it serenely, or even wishing for its arrival. A person who led a natural and unimpaired life see death as a natural, appropriate event, as though it were restful sleep after a hard day's work. In this case, death will be tranquil and*

*easy, just like falling asleep. It will be Dormition". (Kalinovsky, 1991)*

The above quotations demonstrate that the Orthodox outlook sees the idea of afterlife for the soul as an obvious and natural part of existence. Traditional texts even name specific lengths of time for each stage in the soul's new life, e.g. the day when the soul leaves the body, the day when it comes back to take the last look at familiars and friends for the last time before taking leave. Thus, during the first three days after death the soul is releasing itself from the robe of flesh and is making its farewells, taking leave of the relations and of the habitual place. Also, it is during this period of time that the soul goes through redemption as the angels and the demons argue about which of them have the right to take possession of the soul of the deceased. During the next six days the soul is shown the heavenly bliss, and during the following thirty-one days the soul is shown the torments in hell. Eventually, on the fortieth day the soul finds itself before Jesus Christ for the first judgment. Then and there the soul shall be appointed a place in which to abide until the Last Judgment when the Lord will either declare the complete individual (with the body resurrected) His brother or sister, or renounce that person as an embodiment of sin. In the period until the Last Day, the intimate lot of the soul may be influenced (due to the intercession of the Church, of the righteous, of the family and friend), but on the Last Day the fate of the soul shall be decided by God, and nothing will be able to alter it. God's word shall be final. "And the Angels ware by Him that liveth for ever and ever ... that there should be time no longer" (Rev. 10:6). Time implies changes, but everything that is timeless is eternal. Human fate can either be an everlasting life in the joy of being with Christ or an eternal death in the torments of non-being without Christ. These profound ontological notions give rise to the practice of the requiem office for the dead on the ninth day and the fortieth day after demise. Traditionally, on those two days orthodox Christians get together at the table to remember the dead relation, to have a drink, and to speak well of the deceased in observance of the common rule *De mortius aut bene, aut nihil* (of the dead, speak well or say nothing). Nowadays another tradition is being revived, i.e. to go to church on that day and light a requiem candle for the soul of the deceased to be in peace.

The approach of Christian anthropological eschatology can be accepted or rejected, completely or partially. The essential thing however is that the followers of Jesus Christ are united both with the Eternal Life and the Eternal Truth, whereas those who reject Jesus until themselves with the nonexistence in Death. In terms of essential meaning, the notions lead to a choice between the eternal life with Christ or the everlasting death without. There can be no alternative, no middle value: one cannot be half-alive and half-dead at once. One cannot serve God, the God of Light, in the morning, and in the same evening be with His adversary, the Devil of Darkness.

## Works written in the twentieth century on the issue of spiritual life

The discussion above was based on the treatment of spiritual life in the Bible, i.e. in the revelations of the prophets who thousands of years ago, had been in communion with the Supreme Mind. The twentieth century has brought with it an unprecedented number of similar contacts, many of them described in minute detail. The numerous books dealing with the problem of communion and contact have become a distinct part of the world literature. There have been earlier examples, of course. Suffice it to mention the works of Emmanuel Swedenborg (1688-1772), whose theological philosophy forms the basis for the Church of the New Jerusalem, claiming direct mystical communication between this world and the spiritual realm, and affirming Christ as the true God. As for the profound esoteric traditions of the East, mention should be made of the literature on the subject in Sanskrit, the Buddhist writings, books by Ramakrishna (1844-1884), Hindu mystic, a leader of modern Hinduism, and by Vivekananda (original name—Narendranath Datha, 1863-1902. Hindu Vedantist leader and educator). Until the end of the nineteenth century the works of Eastern philosophers were little known in Europe, which was not due to the lack of interest—it must be explained by the general control and the monitoring pressure exerted by the Christian Churches.

Theosophy, occultism, spiritualism, spiritual teachings all put forth an idea of the soul that has a fine structure and is able to travel in the heavenly realm above the Earth.

A particularly important theory was suggested by the Russian-born Yelena Roerich (1879-1955), the great-granddaughter to the Russian Field-Marshal Kutuzov (the commander who defeated Napoleon in 1812), niece to composer Moussorgsky, wife of the artist Nikolai K. Roerich by whom she had had two sons, Svyatoslav and Yuri, outstanding personalities in the arts and science, respectively. She was also the mother of Agni Yogi doctrine and claimed to have had direct mystic communications with the spiritual realms and had recorded the spiritual messages she had received. Her major work is the fourteen-volume "Agni Yogi" ("The Living Ethics" or "The Teachings of Light").

The doctrine suggested by Yelena Roerich deals with global things—from the place of our planet in the Universe to the essence of thought as an energy. It deals with the two principal invisible worlds (the Thin World and the Fiery World) and with the brethren of humankind, who form an invisible hierarchy helping these inhabitants of Earth incessantly. The doctrine also involves the notion of psychic energy carried by people. It rejects the notion of death, stating that "death is no more than a haircut". It exalts the notion of beauty. Below the reader will find some ideas from Yelena Roerich's "Agni Yoga" rendered from the Russian edition published in 1992.

> *"It is the fact of transition that makes people dread the moment of death. But how wonderfully does the spirit rush upwards into the Thin World because it has perceived the transitory character of its existence on the Earth! One should prepare one's spirit for a conscientious estrangement from the Earth... When the fiery spirit is immersed in the overground spheres, it does not avoid the Thin Spheres, because the spirit has experienced a transitory state in space. It is with the feeling of joy that the spirit approaches the Fiery World.*
>
> *One should be considerate of one's last hours on Earth. Very often the last aspiration will determine the next life, as well as the spirit's position in the layers which are to be its abode. It is inadmissible, of course, to summon the spirit back to earth once it has broken off. The tissues, which have set themselves free from the attractive central gravitational force exerted by the Earth, will have to suffer a great strain in order to assimilate themselves once again to the Earth's atmosphere. One should learn to be able to think at exit in the same manner as one used to think at birth. Delays are harmful at birth, and they are equally harmful at death. The fine structure of the new body must be taken into consideration. The wounds inflicted upon the dying will have to be healed in the Thin World. Torments are not caused by death, but they are caused by the living.*
>
> *Astral bodies have their volumes and their weights, and possess many of the properties characteristic of this earthly life. The relativity of earthly knowledge is generally known. To a great extent, the astral bodies retain this relativity, but no sooner have they set themselves free from the earthly cover than the astral bodies acquire the ability of spiritual creativity. "(Agni Yoga, 1992).*

Adherents of occultism have developed an even more elaborate theory of the multiform structure of the human soul. Some occult theories regard the person's existence as occurring on several levels at once, with the physical level being the lowest and the most comprehensible one. The next, ethereal level, is where a person possesses an *ethereal body* that supports the formation and the very existence of the *physical body*. In comparison with the physical body, the ethereal body has a higher degree of reality. It is owing to the movements of the ethereal body that the parts and organs of the human body maintain their forms and shapes. The ethereal body corresponds to the mineral level. All things living possess ethereal bodies. The third component of a person is the astral body. While the physical body cannot retain its form without the assistance of the ethereal body, the power of the ethereal body alone is not sufficient to produce the light of conscience. Taken alone, the ethereal body would only be able to keep the physical body in the vegetable state. When awake, the ethereal body is lit up by the astral body.

The three bodies—physical, ethereal, and astral—are the essence of the corporeal part of the human being. In addition, there is a component that forms the soul. Human self-identity is composed of the perceiving soul, the reasoning soul, and the conscious soul. Then there is a component that is spirit. The spirit is composed of the Self-Spirit, the Life-Spirit, and the Man-Spirit.

At death, the physical body is separated from the ethereal body. The physical body now has to cope on its own, and, unable to do so it is to decay. The ethereal body maintains its communion with the astral body for a few more days, during which period the deceased is in a state allowing it to perceive the experiences and emotions of the astral body. After death, the first experience of the deceased consists of the images of life between physical birth and death. In terms of manifestation, they are quite unlike the same images experienced during the lifetime. To a certain extent, life proceeds backwards during the purification stage, which means that experience starts with the images immediately preceding death, and other images come by one in reverse order until the deceased is able to recall the early childhood. It is not until the deceased has gone through all stages of life—back to the moment of birth—that all the person's longings get purified by the purging fire. Then there is nothing to prevent the deceased from plunging wholly into the spiritual world, which is yet another stage of existence. First the physical body is left behind, then the ethereal body, and finally the time comes for decay of that part of astral body which can only exist in the conscience of the outward physical world.

Consequently, there are three dead bodies: physical, ethereal and astral. The course of a person's life falls into three stages:

1. the period during which the physical and ethereal bodies grow up and mature,

2. the period when the astral body and self-identity also participate in the process of development, and

3. the period when the ethereal and the physical bodies begin to redevelop, i.e. when they start growing backwards. As for the astral body, it participates in the entire process—from birth until death.

Similar theories have been suggested by other thinkers, e.g. Mme. Yelena Petrovna Blavatsky (1831-91) who developed a doctrine about the so-called astral planes that are a sort of stepping stones for the soul to climb on its way to the spiritual realm; also, the authors of the voluminous *works* Urantia *and* Dianetics, as well as many others who claimed to have had direct communication with the Supreme Mind and who were able to write down the reports of their contacts in an understandable and readable manner. We are not going to review those works here and now, nor are we going to substantiate their value. What matters for us here is the general thesis of the self-sufficiency (self-consummation) of the soul, as well as the idea of the soul's existence during a short or a long period of time after the death of the body.

## Scientific views on the issues of immortality

The sages among the humankind have always been able to see the spiritual aspect of the world. They have always believed in God and in immortal spirit. The ancient philosophers, including Plato and Socrates, believed in immortality. Plato taught, "The human spirit is immortal. The hopes and aspirations of the soul are in the next world. A true sage is willing to die so as to start a new life."

Among the true believers in God one can name Sir Isaac Newton, Galileo Galilee, Blaise Pascal, Louis Pasteur, Albert Einstein, Ivan Pavlov, and many other outstanding thinkers and authors. Below are a few quotations from the Russian authors of different times.

*"Only he who never thought seriously of death will not believe in the immortal spirit." (Leo Tolstoy)"The person's life, both private and social, is based on the belief in the immortal soul. It is the su-*

*preme idea, without which neither an individual nor the nation can
ever exist." (Fyodor Dostoyevsky)*
*"I believe that every human being is able to perceive the presence of
God, if only one does not submit oneself to the fuss of everyday life."
(Alexander Solzhenitsyn)*

In the recent decades, the issue of immortality has been widely discussed by the scientists. A further development of scientific views on the problem has been offered by Raymond Moody, E. Kubler-Ross, and by their numerous followers. Their books are so widely known that it does not seem necessary to try and render their contents here. All of them contain discussions of cases of "clinical death". Individuals who have experienced death and have been brought back to life all tell similar stories: they all experienced a separation from the physical body, an instantaneous image of their entire life prior to the moment of separation, the perception of a long tunnel leading up into the heavenly light. If one has been following this review from the very beginning, one will realize that there is nothing novel in such contributions, since the sources cited earlier have all been based on similar recollections, and the book *The Eternal Mysteries of the afterlife* is entirely composed of such recollections, with references to experiences of the holy fathers of early Christian era. Special merit, however, must be given to the books written by Raymond Moody and others, because the authors have awakened the general public to the issue by dealing with it in terms of modern scientific research methods.

A considerable contribution to the study has been made by the school of transpersonal psychology. Of great interest are the observational research conducted by Stanislav Grof, who studied the effects of hallucinogen drugs (LSD in particular) on the human conscience. Dr. Grof was able to detect several levels of conscience, which manifest themselves when the brain is "set free" due to the influence of LSD. While moving from level to level, the individual moves further and further away from the biological nature to approach the Universal cosmic consciousness. The material collected by Dr. Grof and his wife Christina allowed them to draw certain conclusions on the nature of human conscience. He writes in *Beyond the Brain*:

> *"Although there are no clear boundaries and demarcations in the
> realm of consciousness, it seems useful for didactic purposes to dis-
> tinguish four distinct levels or realms of the human psyche and the
> corresponding experiences: (1) the sensory barrier, (2) the individ-
> ual unconscious, (3) the level of birth and death, and (4) the
> transpersonal domain. The experiences of all these categories are*

*quite readily available for most people. They can be observed in sessions with psychedelic drugs and in various modern approaches of experiential psychotherapy using breathing, music, dance, and body work. Laboratory mind-altering techniques, such as biofeedback, sleep deprivation, sensory isolation or sensory overload, and various kinesthetic devices can also induce many of these phenomena. A wide spectrum of ancient and Oriental spiritual practices are specifically designed to facilitate their occurrence. Many experiences of this kind can also occur during spontaneous episodes of non-ordinary states of consciousness. The entire experiential spectrum related to the four realms has also been described by historians and anthropologists with respect to various shamanic procedures, aboriginal rites of passage and healing ceremonies, death-rebirth mysteries, and trance dancing in ecstatic religions." (Grof, 1985)*

Grof's conclusions are directly connected with the issue of death and afterlife. On entering the realm of conscience, the person crosses the barrier of individual death to become a particle of the Universal Mind, and the person's conscience appears to be immortal. Moreover, it gets involved in the general development process taking place in the global realm of conscience. The conclusions suggest an explanation of the instances of transmigration (reincarnation) remembered by certain individuals—deja vu events, and also to help explain extraordinary latent faculties in human being which manifest themselves in moments of mortal danger, extreme situations or special inducements.

*"Some other transpersonal phenomena involve transcendence of spatial rather than temporal barriers. Here belong the experiences of merging with another person in a state of dual unity...or expanding one's consciousness to the extent that it seems to encompass all of humanity. In a similar way, one can transcend the limits of the specifically human experience and tune to what appears to be the consciousness of animals, plants, or even inanimate objects and processes. In the extreme, it is possible to experience the consciousness of all creation, of our planet, of the entire material universe. An important category of transpersonal experiences involving transcendence of time/or space are the various ESP phenomena, such as out-of-body experiences, telepathy, precognition, clairvoyance, and clairaudience, and space and time travel." (Grof, 1985)*

Dr. Grof's research allowed him to put forth a new approach to the understanding of the human role in the Universe.

*"...the exclusive image of the human being as nothing but a biological machine is no longer tenable. In serious logical conflict with this*

*traditional model, the new data supports quite unambiguously the view that has been held by the mystical traditions of all ages: under certain circumstances, human beings can also function as vast fields of consciousness, transcending the limitations of the physical body, of Newtonian time and space, and of linear causality." (Grof, 1985)*

At the same time, Dr. Grof's work ushers in a new way to an understanding of the internal causes and suggests a new treatment for various neuroses. This also refers to such mental illness as thanatophobia, an extreme fear of death. All cases of thanatophobia go through episodes of mortal dread, which are frequently mistaken for the onset of a heart attack, apoplexy, or asphyxia. The regular checkups that the patients seek do not reveal any organic diseases. Their complaints are purely subjective, because the patients suffer from sensations and emotions existing in their empirical memories (caused by bodily traumas, including the traumas at birth), rather than by the current physical process. Of course, their sufferings are real. The only means of rescue is to bravely face the recurring gestalt (by means of active technique). Thus, thanatophobia may be cured through sensations of death and rebirth.

Thoughts of death may exert a strong influence on the mind (psyche) and, consequently, on the behavior of an individual. It should be noted that the influence is not directly related either with the age or with the intellectual level. Dr. Grof writes about this phenomenon citing the lives of two outstanding scientists, Sigmund Freud and Alfred Adler.

*"Freud postulated in his final theoretical formulations the existence of death instinct as a decisive force in the psyche. His biological emphasis prevented him from seeing the possibility of psychological transcendence of death, and he created a gloomy and pessimistic image of human existence. The theme of death also played an important role in his personal life, since he suffered from a severe thanatophobia. Adler's life and work were also very strongly influenced by the problem of death. He saw the inability to prevent and control death as the deepest core of the feeling of inadequacy." (Grof, 1985)*

Dr. Grof is not alone in his speculations. Increasingly, scientists all over the world concede to the necessity of changing the western scientific paradigm and including in it an expanded view of human consciousness. Most of the proposed systems agree on the following major levels of existence: (1) *physical,* involving non-living matter/energy; (2) *biological,* focusing on living, sentient matter/energy; (3) *psychological,* dealing with mind, ego, and logical thinking; (4) *subtle,* comprising psychic and archetypal phenomena; (5) *casual,* characterized by formless radiance and perfect transcendence, and (6) *absolute consciousness* and suchness of all the levels of the spectrum. In particular, in Wilber's model (Wilber, 1982), phenomenal worlds are created from the original unity by progressive reduction and enfolding of higher structures into the lower. In this, Wilber follows exclusively the text of *Bardo Thödol*, described here earlier, which represents the movement from the highest to the lowest levels, or *Bardos,* of the human soul at the time of death. A more detailed survey of existing scientific ideas is given in Part 3 of this book.

It should be noted that the true science has never opposed spirituality. Voltaire's atheism was a revolt against the clerical absolutism, and beneath his atheist clothes Voltaire was a common man struggling for his right of free will. As the quintessence of atheism, Marxism rejected all religions, and at the same time it acquired all properties of a religion—a belligerent and intolerant one at that. That quality of Marxism was pointed out by the Russian thinker Sergiy N. Bulgakov who wrote in 1903:

> *"...the doctrine has many features of a strictly religious teaching. Although it denounces any religion as a manifestation of 'a bourgeois ideology', Marxism is, to a certain extent, an obvious substitute for religion. The Marxist eschatology is in its doctrine of revolution, the Marxist 'paradise' is Communism, the Marxist 'chosen people' is the proletariat. Marxism proclaim capitalism to be the Devil, and the Marxist leaders are their Messiahs—their martyrs suffering for their beliefs. Under the cover of superficial scientific robes, the Marxist teaching tries to quench the religious thirst by religious methods. For, even when deprived of religion, the human being cannot help suffering from his or her separation from the world as a whole entity. The individual longs for an organic unification—for a substitute of the Church communion. That is the reason why such an individual will accept Socialism easily and readily." (Bulgakov, 1903)*

The lines above were written long before the movement started to regard, revere, and worship Marx and Lenin as deities, long before the idea of a Socialist Mausoleum was materialized, long before the "Legendary Lives" of the ideological leaders were written and their obligatory portraits replaced icons in every home, with their obligatory statues in every public square. Joseph Stalin, formerly a student in a theological seminary, had led the Communist religion to its culmination when he declared Lenin to be the Communist god with himself as the god's prophet. Characteristically, the central symbol of the Communist religion was the leader's mummified corpse placed in a glass sarcophagus for people to worship it ecstatically. In thousands upon thousands, common folk would queue for long hours despite the cold weather only to take a look at the mummy while reverently passing by it.

Soviet regime was based on oppression and death. More than occasionally, the problem of life and death was essentially the central theme in the works of outstanding Russian theologians of the twentieth century: Nikolai Berdyayev, Paul Florensky, Vladimir Solovyev, Nikolai Fedorov, Vladimir Rosanov, who considered the issue in the context of philosophical concept of time.

Ancient Greek philosophers related time to the inevitable retributive justice and unavoidable vengeance, whereas the Russian religious thinkers related time as evil, punishment for the primordial sin and for the injustice towards the ancestors. Berdyayev called time an illness of death—a cause decay and death. Hence the opposition to time which, as the Russian philosophers suggested, could be conquered along with death, finiteness and decay either by means of religious faith (Florensky), love and spirituality (Solovyev), freedom and creativity (Berdyayev) or else an active resurrection of the ancestors (Fedorov). The latter conception is a combination of the traditional Christian idea of the resurrection of the dead with the idea of hope inspired by the technological advances and scientific discoveries.

Traditions of Russian philosophy differ fundamentally from those of Western-European philosophies. The European existentialists share a concern for the personal experiences of individuals, centering on the transitory character of the mankind's finite existence. Russian philosophers, on the other hand, hold that eternity is a value of absolutely primary importance. Russian philosophy essentially defies time. In Russian theology and philosophy, the problem of transitory existence (existence in time) has always been transformed into variations of the eternal problem of love and death. In this respect, various doctrines have been suggested: in one (suggested by Rosanov), the way towards the goal is achieved by means of sexual love, which is considered a neutral origin of the species, the erotic element and the source of new life. In another (suggested by Fedorov) immortality is gained through resurrection of the ancestors—which will overcome time itself, and with it—the humankind's finite life span and bodily degradation. Berdyayev holds that time is a foul infinitude. Fedorov hopes for resurrection and continued earthly existence; Berdyayev hopes for its defeat and terminal cessation.

The ideas of the two latter philosophers manifest themselves in the two different concepts of infinity: the ordinary and the metaphysical. The former suggests an infinite future; the latter suggests an escape from it. From the religious and philosophical point of view, "...an infinite life in this world would have no sense. The positive meaning of death is that the consummation of life cannot be realized in time—not even infinite time, let alone finite. Life can only be consummated in eternity — only beyond the time limit"(Berdyaev,1991). Eternity in the sense of immortality is not the future. The future is death.

Many contemporary Russian philosophers hold similar views on the problem of life and death. Suffice is to mention the works of Demichev, Uvarov, Stolovich, Friauf. In a recent philosophical publication, the doctrine is laid out as follows:

> "We split the world in two: the 'before' and the 'after.' The great split in the human conscience cannot perceive the monism of the Universe: it is not able to project death as a continuation of life. We tend to view, as if from aside, the process of body degradation, decay and ultimate disintegration, picturing our soul, able to break away from the body, as the immortal 'Self.' We imagine the body as a trivial piece of substance, unworthy of our sorrow if it decays and perishes. All is perishable but the soul. The soul is not a part of the dispute on life and death—it is beyond, without, not of our Time... In order to reach the supreme ideal, it is necessary to go through the ecstasy of death that is illumination, epiphany, and you will see. The ideal world will present itself as the creator's creation, and, as you fall into the abyss of death, you are no longer a body plus soul, you are a spirit and an angel. The tale of death is captivating, substantial and permanent." (The Forms and Shapes of Thanatos, 1991. 1992.1993. )

## Response of the Orthodox Church to contemporary contributions

The Orthodox Church reacted against the works of Raymond Moody and his followers. Incidentally, the response did not come from Russia, where the political situation in the 1970s allowed no theological disputes. The reaction came from the United States of America—from the hieromonk Seraphim Rose, born into a typically Protestant family and converted to the Orthodox Church in 1961 at twenty-six years of age. In a book published in 1982 he offered detailed analyses of the modern 'out-of-body' experience, UFO-contacts, and the ancient and contemporary writings on occultism and mysticism. He does not actually deny the reality of experiences described in the works in question, but his judgment is unequivocal:

1. These are merely 'extra-corporeal' states, well-known, especially in occult literature, and occurring in recent years with increasing frequency to ordinary people, not otherwise related with occultism. However, in effect, these states tell us almost nothing about what goes on with the soul after death other than that it continues to exist and to have a conscience.

2. The sphere where the soul goes in the beginning, upon first leaving the body, is not the heaven or hell, it is a region close to earth, referred to by various names: 'other side', 'Bardo plane' (Tibetan Book of the Dead), 'Realm of the Spirits' (Swedenborg and spirits), 'Area II' (Monroe), or, in the Christian orthodoxy language, the sub-celestial aerial kingdom inhabited by fallen spirits, who earnestly attempt to mislead people to their end.

3. The beings who can be encountered in this area are always—or almost always—ghosts, whether they are summoned via a medium or by occult means, or encountered during the extra-corporeal existence. These are not the angels, since angels dwell in the heavens, and only transit through this area as God's messengers. These are not the souls of the dead, since these dwell in the heavens or in hell, and would only pass through upon their death on their way to their judgment.

4. Experiments in this realm cannot be trusted, and certainly cannot be judged by their appearance. Even those who are firm in their Christian orthodox beliefs may be easily fooled by the fallen air spirits, and those who enter it uninformed are easy prey for them. (Paraphrased from Rose, 1991)

The place, where the soul comes just after death, is not Paradise or Hell, but a special area close to the Earth where the evil spirits are living. These spirits try to cheat the person's soul to get it ruined. Angels cannot be met in this area, as they live in the Sky and only pass by it when coming to the God. The souls of the dead stay in this area only temporally on their way to the Judgment-seat. Hence, in this area only the evil-spirits — Hellhounds — can be met, and all experiences are induced by these spirits.

Fortunately, not all Orthodox priests are as categorical in their judgments. In the preface to a Russian book titled *The Transition*, the Moscow priest Alexander Borisov, Ph.D., a Doctor of Biology, writes the following:

*"One of the greatest achievements made in the second half of the twentieth century are the modern advances in medical science which have given us an opportunity to see beyond the curtain of death for a period of five to ten minutes (the period of resuscitation), to make certain that there is a new life to be lived beyond that curtain. It may very well happen that in the years to come we shall be able to learn more and more about life after death. In any case, one thing is certain: God has granted us a revelation which is in accordance with the present level of scientific thought. What shall be our response to this revelation? The answer will depend on the intuition, sensitivity, maturity, and free will of each of us." (Kalinovsky, 1991).*

This idea can be traced all through Kalinovsky's book:

*"The main achievement of recent years has been the fact that the medical doctors studying the problem of resuscitation have supported the Christian teaching on the life of the soul. The first step, which is also the most important one, has been irrevocably taken: after the death of the body, life continues. This fact has been confirmed by the medical science as well as by theology." (Kalinovsky, 1991).*

Indeed, if, in their after-death experiences, they had met the devils or the fallen spirits, then the human beings would have been influenced by the evil spirits and their tricks. After their revival, such persons would have stayed in the power of the evil spirits and would have behaved accordingly. Such individuals would be full of bile, of wickedness, of hatred, and of the desire to hurt the humankind in every imaginable way. Examples of such behavior have been shown more than once in American films, e.g. "The Exorcist". In fact, the revived persons behave in a quite different manner. Among those who have experienced death and resuscitation, most people have undergone a spiritual transformation. Quite frequently, the spiritual transformation is complete: they begin to perceive the brightness and preciousness of life, their attitude towards other people becomes all kindness and affection, they begin to think of others and to take care of them, they may be said to have thrown away everything vain and superficial and meaningless, they become instrumental in rendering Love and Happiness. By no means can these qualities be the impact of evil spirits. It is important to note that this thought was mentioned in Moody's first book (Moody 1976).

Reverend Alexander Menn, an outstanding Christian Orthodox thinker (dreadfully murdered in 1991 by an unknown killer), writes of the afterlife:

*"For a Christian, the idea of uniqueness of every person excludes the idea of a transmigrating soul. Yet, in the Christian conscience, the doctrine of reincarnation is important in a different sense. What is that sense? Jesus Christ said, "… If any man will come after me, let him deny himself and take up his cross, and follow me." (Matt. 16:24) Which implies a moral, rather than a metaphysical, transformation, an ability to leave the prison cell of one's own Self in order to acquire the capacity for empathy without losing one's self-identity. For he who gives himself to others will benefit from it. In fact, the notion of reincarnation transforms the idea of immortal soul into something earthly, something material, whereas the mystery goes beyond the earthly existence. Here we deal with a continuous development of the person, rather than with recurrent episodes. Regardless of the number of the worlds, the individual undergoes a development and improvement in each of them… If a person has left much undone in this world, it means that he or she will be granted opportunities to do it in other worlds with other dimensions. The road to the goal is endless. The development is boundless. Jesus said that Man must be perfect, for Our Father in heaven is perfect. It means that there are no bounds to our development and perfection. It also means that something very important is conceived in this earthly existence.*

One should not believe, however, that the separation of the soul from the body at death must signify the individual's liberation. It is not so. God has created us as beings in whom the fickle matter, the Nature, and the immortal Spirit are married. The idea of Man and his mission is the union of all worlds. We unite two different worlds—this is why the teachings of the Church include not only the idea of immortal spirit (which other religions share), but also the idea of resurrection of the dead for a life to come in the new age." (Menn, 1991)

## Conclusion

Several conclusions can be drawn from the above discussion.

The esoteric beliefs, the occult beliefs, and the religious teachings of all times and of all peoples concur that death does not terminate the life of the soul.

According to various doctrines, existence of the soul after death can take different forms. However, all doctrines are agreed that there exists a tie between one's earthly life and one's afterlife of the soul, and the latter is the continuation of the former on a different level.

The soul does not leave the body at once. Various terms have been assigned to this process by different doctrines, generally from two to nine days. Within this period, the soul is connected with the body. Sometimes the soul is able to return into the body, and the person can be revived for a further life on Earth. In the vast majority of cases, however, the transfer of the soul irreversible. The soul undergoes a transformation, and acquires a new spiritual experience, which determines the soul's further existence. Even so, the soul continues to be connected with the body it has left.

All beliefs on the afterlife of the soul elicit response, support, and confirmation by the contemporary scientific thought and practice.

# Mountaineering diary

Dry, inflexible experimental approach alone cannot sufficiently cover the subject matter of this book. For every human being the topic is too heavily loaded with intricate conceptual systems dealing with morality, philosophy and ethics. Thus, in order to relate the author's personal point of view on the subject of death, his notes have been incorporated into the text, originally written in a dry, factual manner. The notes, which are placed at suitable intervals throughout the scholarly text, are meant to dilute the somber subject. It is entirely up to the reader to ponder over the author's reflections or skip over them.

The collapse of the empire of Soviet Union drove many of its citizens to a careful consideration of Death. Until then, the hustle and bustle of everyday life, the ideological din intentionally produced by the authorities had really left no time for serious thinking. To most Soviet people death seemed a stranger, a foreign element—something entirely out of Soviet context and, if possible, something to be avoided. The society was trained to regard Death as an accident, misfortune, and generally an unlucky turn of events breaking the smooth flow of idyllic Soviet life. Voltaire and Rousseau, and later Karl Marx and Friedrich Engels had created the powerful atheistic movement, which was then elevated by the Soviet rulers Lenin and Stalin to the ranks of religion. During seventy years of the Soviet regime, this movement managed to change radically not only the proletarian world's outlook, but also the entire moral landscape of the whole Russian nation—or, to be precise, of what remained of the Russian nation after the revolution and the ensuing political tyranny. Genuine faith was out of the question in Soviet society. Rationalism and skepticism had been implanted in the Soviet minds. Hence the general attitude towards Death. It was seen as the edge of the abyss, some black curtain separating our bright world of the living from the bottomless non-existence of the dead. This morality was reinforced by official propaganda, which painted the image of cloudless happiness in the country where nothing bad could ever happen by definition, where all criminality was eradicated at the root, where there were no industrial calamities in the coal mines or elsewhere, where people died peacefully only at an advanced age and after long, happy lives.

These illusions were cruelly crushed by the events of recent years. A wave of hatred and bloodshed swept through the population of the former Soviet republics, through major cities and the countryside of mainland Russia and the adjoining lands. Crime—both organized and random—was ubiquitous. Accidents, explosions and catastrophes follow one another in a continuous succession. The parliamentary riot in Moscow on October 3-4, 1993, has made it clear that in their struggle for power, party politicians of every hue share a lack of concern about the fate and livelihood of their compatriots. Naturally, the thought of encountering death is ubiquitous as well, bringing the citizen to the very hard question: 'What does death mean?'

Any adult has faced Death in its claim on one's near and dear, whether family or friend, and any adult has attended a funeral at the cemetery. For the most part, these events have been seen as tragic incidents not connected with life at all, which are beyond the pattern of everyday activities and emotions. Time flies, and only some memories and the traditionally tidy gravestone remain, while life goes on, taking its normal course. For the general populace, Life and Death are wide apart from each other.

Awareness of death came to me at the age of twenty-one, when mountaineering was the greatest pleasure of my life. I used to make regular trips to the mountains three or four times a year, always with several other friends from my mountaineering club, and always to increasingly difficult climbs. In the summer of 1973, two young climbers from my club lost their lives in the mountains. Roped in a pair, they were ascending a steep ice slope, when suddenly the second man in the pair stumbled and fell. When one falls on a steep ice slope, it is virtually impossible to stop sliding. The leader was caught unawares when the rope pulled him down. The two were sliding faster and faster, now side by side, now apart, now pushing one another with the sharp-pointed crampons fastened to their climbing boots. They tried to hold on to the surface only to feel the skin stripped off their hands. Finally they struck the ice blocks on the icefall below, and stopped. One of them died right there, the other lived long enough to arrive at the hospital. They both were strong, healthy, and young—just over twenty. I knew them both well.

The emotional impact on me was so great that I began to see the two sides of mountaineering at once. Before the accident I only saw the thrill. Training in the fantastically beautiful mountains, opposing wrath of the elements brought out real men and made friends for life. Now I saw the other aspect, the mortal danger of it all. I had known of the danger hypothetically: after each climbing season we had a special session at the club, where we were informed in detail of all incidents and accidents, and their causes, with subsequent discussions on what ought to have been done and of how it could have been avoided. Books on mountaineering contained scores of episodes described in detail. We all knew that ours was the most dangerous sport, with the risks always great irrespective of the country. In the United States, for example, the annual death rate was 56 per 10,000 climbers according to the report published by the National Safety Council for the years 1984-89. By comparison, hang gliding (the second on the danger list) took an annual toll of 11.4 per 10,000. But never before had death come so near to me; never before had I seen my friends killed.

I must admit I then had my doubts whether it was really worth it. Why should I take the risks? I also became interested in the Eastern philosophies and started spending hours in the public library. I read books on Hinduism, Buddhism, Zoroastrianism, Confucianism, and Zen. Few works on the subject were available in Russian, and I had to read most of them in English. The aching void in my heart was gradually being filled with ideas from these books. I had a lot of material to analyze, to make comparisons, to find parallels. Eventually I developed a philosophy of my own, which I will call the philosophy of optimistic fatalism. It was a hodgepodge of other peoples' ideas (from Epicureans to Zen-Buddhists), which I had built up on the foundation of Christianity. Before I write about it at length, I will draw a general analogy.

Let us imagine an ant crawling up the trunk of a tree. From the ant's point of view, there is no telling if the tree is tall or short, if it has many branches or few etc. The brave ant is climbing higher and higher, until it turns, without thinking, to continue along a branch. This is a critical moment, a turning point in the ant's life, for all the other parts of the tree have just been cut off. The ant can never explore other boughs, branches, twigs, or leaves. It is certainly for the ant to decide to retrace his steps and take a different route. The way back is always open, but the forward movement makes the idea of retreat more and more difficult and problematic. So the ant advances onto a smaller branch, than along a twig, and eventually onto a green leaf at the very end of the twig. The forward movement has been concluded, and the ant will stay on the small leaf to the end of his short life.

Human beings are likewise engaged in a forward movement which often depends on their own choices, actions, laziness, mistakes etc., but life on the whole is always in the hands of God. It is for the Lord to decide who is to be born into the Rockefeller family and who is to be born into the family of a peasant in the Siberian village at the end of the earth. It is for Him to determine how long a newborn baby is to live, whether he or she shall die at twenty or will live to be eighty. I suggest, however, that the word "determine" should be used with reservations. God's decisions need not be the only determinant factor. The life of a small insect (like the ant above) may come to an untimely end due to different factors, e.g. a sudden rush of wind, a drop of sticky sap, a hungry bird. Similarly, no human being can be certain how long his/her life is likely to continue, because it may discontinue quite suddenly, at any moment. Anything may happen tomorrow: a brick may fall on my head from above and kill me, a drunken driver may hit my car and kill me, an emergency blood transfusion may infect me with AIDS and kill me slowly. All events, everything that happens to us, should be regarded as Acts of God. I find it true both about Death and Life, with one difference between them, i.e. practically every situation in life can be lived through, can be overcome, can be forgotten, and things may so change in the course of time that life will appear brighter and more beautiful than ever before. All around the world, a saying persists in many tongues and variations: 'Time heals all wounds.'

This reminds me of mountaineering again. Whenever the weather changes for the worse, one can go to one's tent and wait patiently, making the most of it in the warmest corner. One cannot do the same about Death. You cannot wait and allow it to pass by. The arrival of Death is purposeful: he comes to take his toll away to his own world. All the same, Death seems to be playing his game according to certain rules. I developed a system of notions after my twenty-plus years of mountaineering and rock-climbing. My system agrees, quite naturally, with many customs, beliefs and superstitions existing in various parts of the world. I will list the notions supplying them with examples from my favorite sport, mountaineering, because it is in the risky undertaking like mountaineering that the latent laws and regularities manifest themselves faster and brighter that anywhere else. One and the same process may take a period of many months on land or the time taken by one climb in the mountain.

More often than not, Death gives a warning. A sign spelling out "No Entrance" may be said to appear to those who can read Death's language. From time immemorial people knew of the sign language of Death, and have always looked for such signs, especially at times of imminent great events or calamities. Before major military campaigns, the great captains of ancient times would ask the priests to prophesy what the future had in store for them. The priests, or sages, or shamans, or holy men by any other name would all use different methods. Some trusted the positions of the stars in the sky, others would study the ashes of the sacred bonfire, still others would practice fortune-telling from reading sacred signs on the sacred animals' guts. Such signs as thunderstorm, hurricane, eclipse of the sun, and other manifestations of the fury of the elements have always been considered as signs of warning. Actually, the outward signs have been looked upon as sort of traffic lights, as certain posts marking the way to the truth, whereas the real guiding force has been the inner voice, or, to be more precise, the voice of God passing on his will.

It could be fatal to rely upon the outward signs only. The son of Nostradamus, who also practiced astrological prophecies, was punished by death for a wrong military forecast. None of the numerous modern Russian astrologers were able to foretell the dramatic political events in this country in August 1991 or in October 1993. They were observing the positions of the stars mechanically without any deep penetration into the heart of the matter. The warning sign of Death may manifest itself as an event, phenomenon, or incident, but more often it is an inner feeling, mental awareness, superstitious belief. All manifestations of superstitious beliefs make sense if they are really penetrated into. Animals present us with a good example. Cats are the most sensitive pets in terms of sensing the energy. The cat is able to perceive its master's energy. The cat will show pleasure and affection by purring and keeping close to those whose energy field is powerful and good-natured. The cat will come to the owner if he or she is in need of energetic feedback. The cat will run away from a person surrounded by a rigid field giving out a pricking sensation. This hardly agrees with the general superstition that a black cat is a bad omen.

The most telling outward sign is the general character of a process and the coincidence by which the seemingly insignificant events happen to come together. Taken alone, each of the minor events may seem a trifle. When they are recurring frequently and regularly, the trifles add up, and this can only mean that the process has taken a wrong route. If this is the case, one ought to either try and change the route or step aside.

In 1983 our team of six young sportsmen went to the faraway Central Pamir gorge to conquer a rock face which had not yielded to any climbers. Bad omens started appearing from the very beginning of this adventure. The warnings of evil fortune were many. As we approached the site, our mule slipped on the path, and we had to carry the load on our own shoulders. While we were having trouble with the mule, the sack with sugar got lost mysteriously. It was never found, and we had to have our tea with only the recollections of the sugar. On the very first day, when we just started making a reconnaissance of the work to be done and of the route to be covered, a small rock rolling down the side of the mountain hit one of us, cutting the tendons in his foot. It took us the rest of the day to carry him to where the shepherds were with their flocks and then to transport him, on a borrowed mule, to the main camp below. On the second day, during a vertical ascent, a screwgate snapped under the weight of another fellow, who was saved only by the safety loop on the rope—but not before suffering a seven-meter fall. On the third day I found myself suffering from food poisoning, with the usual symptoms of severe vomiting and diarrhea. I grew weak as a baby, reduced to crawling from hook to hook, out of breath after each move. These events were crowned that same day by a thunderstorm.

The five of us were sitting huddled in our tent fastened to the pitons on a small rock ledge in the middle of the rock face, at a distance of 400 meters above level ground. The heavy rain, the howling wind, the thunder and lightening striking almost simultaneously, as they normally do in the heart of the storm, vividly demonstrating the fury of the elements and suggesting thoughts of an unfortunate outcome. We were getting wet to the skin and we could not help being alarmed at the howls of the wind trying to break the strong ropes. By midnight the storm had abated, but the clouds were still shedding rain. In the sunshine of the next morning we were drying our clothes and arguing about what had better be done. My friend and I argued that we had much better descend immediately. Two others insisted that we climb on. One did not speak up.

It was not the thunderstorm that had alerted me, but the sequence of annoying trifles which seemed to warn repeatedly: 'Do not advance. STOP AND RETREAT.' Those for the ascent of the mountain said that we had much to do, that the most difficult part of the rock face was behind us, that the sun was shining and we should be triumphantly coming back the day after the next. Eventually, I used my right of the leader to stop the debate, "Let's call it a day. Take off the ropes. We are going down." Four hours later we were back on the ground, and the thousand-meter-tall wall remained unconquered. With doubts gnawing at my heart, I kept asking myself, "Did I make the right call? Oughtn't we to have struggled through? How shall we explain to the others why we backed out?" In the evening we were in the shepherds' quarters. No sooner had we gotten there than a horrific storm broke out, much more powerful than before. If it was so terrible down where we were now, what was it like up there, I wondered. The weather stayed bad for four days. As we discussed it again down in the main camp, we concluded we had been rather clever about backing out of our expedition. Two years earlier, a group of rock climbers from Rostov froze to death on the rock face under similar circumstances: their leader would not give in, he would conquer the mountain at any price. He was the only survivor.

# Brief description of the experimental data

## Research technique

Preparation for experimental work was based on the following fundamental principles:

- data reliability
- objectivity
- possibility of independent reproduction of the results.

The experiment was organized as follows. The subject, delivered to the experimental site within 1-3 hours from the time of death, was taken to the experimental room. The left hand of the subject was fixed on the electrode by means of a restricting device which ensured a stationary position of the hand and fingers throughout the experimental session. Every hour, the Kirlian discharge characteristics of left-hand fingers were registered. The experimental process consisted of 3 quasi-independent steps:

- the preparation, including the mounting and checking of the equipment, object selection and installation;
- experiment itself and draft material processing;
- computer processing of the experimental data.

Special measures were taken to ensure repeatability of the results, and to minimize the effect of operator qualification and emotional state and the environment, especially with respect to the electromagnetic environmental situation during the experiment. The second part of this book provides samples of environmental electromagnetic situations.

## Main results

Ten experimental sessions, to be discussed in detail in Part 3, were performed in 1993, each taking from three to five days. Subjects included both males and females, varying in age from 19 to 70.

The experiments immediately showed that the deceased bodies exhibited a specific Kirlian glow intensity, variable in time, but no qualitative difference existed between the discharge glow of living and the deceased. We were unable to discern any special features of the glow associated with the deceased bodies. The types of glow varied within a wide range, with transitions from one type to another. Glow intensity was lower for deceased bodies, but did not drop to zero level—only to some fixed value. Taken out of context, it would have been impossible for any specialist to discriminate *a priori* between the discharge photos of living and the deceased.

We believe the main result of our experiments to be the experimental discovery of the correlation between the type and cause of death and the character of the discharge characteristic associated with the particular subject. In order to evaluate the meaning of the presented data, it is first necessary to classify it into groups. The most natural classification principle seems to be in accordance with the amplitude of curve oscillations, which yields three groups of data (examples of these curves may be seen in Fig. 1.1):

- Curves with relatively weak oscillation amplitude (amplitude of oscillations is within 600 units);
- Curves with relatively weak oscillation amplitude and with one pronounced peak;
- Curves with large amplitude (amplitude of oscillation is more than 600 units) with oscillations of long duration.

Now we can see a very interesting feature: each of the above groups is characterized by a specific death cause:

- "calm, natural" death caused by the condition of body tissues.
- "violent" death—e.g. as a result of a traffic accident, with scull/brain injury.

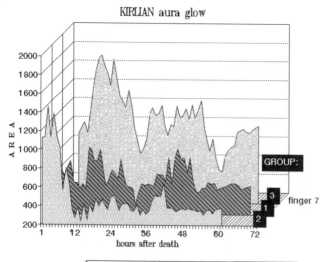

KIRLIAN aura glow

GROUP:
3
1
2
finger 7

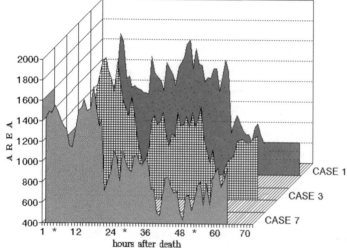

CASE 1
CASE 3
CASE 7

*Fig. 1.1 Examples of Krlian glow intensity curves*

. "unexpected" death as a result of some tragic circumstances which could have been avoided in more favorable conditions.

We should stress that the above division is rather tentative and in no case final—the data sample is too little to proclaim these associations definitive. It's quite possible that the principle of this classification will substantially change at some later instance.

At the same time it is evident that the *moment of transition* through the last threshold is determined by many factors, which are often random: whether there is a medicine at hand; whether medical aid was timely; the person's stress level, etc. At any given stage there is too little data for final classification, and, therefore, the groups named above should be seen as preliminary. However even such preliminary analysis sometimes sheds a new light on data and lays a foundation for further experiments. Let us note the main features of curves common to each group.

Group I. On the curve one might allocate two segments: oscillations exceeding benchmark level and comparable with benchmark; duration of the first segment is from 16 to 55 hours, it is scarcely expedient to allocate any features to these sites.

Group II. Explicitly pronounced peak in one case corresponds to the first 8 hours after death, in the other case—the end of the first day; oscillations come to benchmark level approximately two days after the death.

Group III. In this group the most explicitly represented features common for all three cases are as follows:

- high amplitude and duration of oscillations as compared with the previous groups;
- reduction of amplitude from the beginning to the end of experiment—peaks at night from 9 p.m., of various rate and duration;
- local glow drop at the end of the first day and a sharp drop at the end of the second day.

Allocated groups are also distinguished by a common nature of the glow at the beginning and at the end of the experiment.

The obtained set of data raises many questions. How is it to be interpreted? What factors can be connected with the observed phenomena? What hypotheses can we formulate from this? Data obtained raise a lot of questions. What does it all mean? With what factors can the phenomena observed be connected? How can it be interpreted? And naturally, the first question one should answer: how reliable is this data, is this not caused by experimental errors or registration of simple physiological processes? Let us improvise on the theme of the data obtained, putting together possible interpretations, objections and arguments.


## Objections and arguments

The first objection is the one we can hear from practical-minded materialists: "This is all nonsense and a waste of time and money. A physical body two days after death can show no activity besides the processes of decomposition. Noted oscillations means nothing but insignificant fluctuations determined by photo materials and data processing errors."

This argument is quite easy to answer. Probably, further critics will find more than one error in our experimental technique, but as a first step it seems to us quite satisfactory. This is confirmed by the holistic nature of the obtained results, for example the glow drop from the beginning of the experiment to its end, though the drop is not identical for all cases but is dependent on the situation. If it depended on the experimenter, this drop would have been more or less smooth and identical for all cases. And in some cases we observed even a rise of that characteristic in the end! Besides, as was noted in the description of the technique, a picture of a benchmark object—a little bottle with physiological solution was taken simultaneously with object discharge pictures. The benchmark glow curve is the most direct method of error calibration. As was shown in the previous chapter, the benchmark oscillation range is substantially smaller than the range for the most "calm" case. Comparison with meteorological data also demonstrates the absence of any appreciable influences of this factor on experimental data. So we see no reason to doubt the reliability of presented results.

After this explanation, our materialistic critic can offer the following argument: "All the presented data do not cause doubt from the experimental technique's point of view, but what they register is nothing more than residual physiology activity of muscle tissues transforming in the process of decomposition. Processes individual for each sample take place in tissue, for example, dehydration and wrinkling, dependent upon epidermis age and environmental conditions. To speak of any connection of the data obtained with the former owner of these tissues is meaningless."

The main answer to this argument as it seems to me is the nature of the data obtained—primarily their division into three groups, correlating with the nature and reason of death. The most interesting are the features noted in the third group. The physiological characteristics measured after death vary in the first hours and further on either remain constant or change smoothly, as smooth curves. We could find the oscillatory processes anywhere and what is more, the processes similar to those obtained. At this stage it is early to make any conclusions, but it is known that oscillatory processes with periodic rises and drops during several hours are characteristic of systems with high activity.

At the same time, if we registered only the processes of dehydration and transformation of body tissues, they would correlate with individual features and age, and the temperature in the room. But this correlation is absent. Really, if in Groups I and II people of almost the same age are represented, in the most interesting Group III age varies : 18, 49 and 56 years. The body characteristics differ as well: a heavy-build man in Case 1 a fat crumbly man in Case 3 and a young girl in Case 7. In accordance with body tissue state, two young males from Cases 4 and 5 should have correlated with Cases 1 and 3, but the curve characteristics for these cases bear much more resemblance to Group I.

Perhaps in the future experiments it is essential to make direct measurements of body tissues changes.

The temperature in the experimental room, as was mentioned above, during the first seven experiments was constant, experiments 8,9 were conducted at different temperatures at night and during daytime; however this did not influence the results: curves 8 and 9 were the most "quiet". Naturally, the presented experimental material is entirely insufficient for any unequivocal conclusions, but we have already noted and repeatedly emphasized that our book is only an approach to the theme, an introduction, requiring purposeful and extended development. A strong argument would be the investigation of isolated organism tissues after the death, preferably a more or less large unit. At the given stage we were not able to organize such an experiment. But some years ago we conducted a cycle of experiments on bovine tissue glow registration, both frozen and in different stages of spoilage. Reproducible changes of glow were obtained, but, on the one hand they concerned only brightness changes or crown size changes and never resulted in occurrence of any abnormal bursts or spots. On the contrary, these changes were orderly and smooth, with regular direction. No oscillatory processes were found.

And at last we do not exclude the possibility that we will be accused of juggling and shuffling facts. To this argument I can object nothing, and it seems to me useless. The idea of this book is addressed to an open-minded person who is willing to look beyond our present-day understanding and knowledge, to accept new ideas and facts.

# Flight of imagination on the wings of experimental data

*Alas, our fate is carefree and merciless*
*As a child: with a smile she erases secretly*
*The pictures, that mind draws for a heart*
*With the thin paint of our secret hopes.*
*Hala Satavachan (I millennium AD)*

The second, 'scientific' part of this book presents detailed experimental material in the sober academic style, steering clear of emotions and opinions. Here, on the other hand, the author discards the academic bonds for a time and will improvise a little on the theme of the data obtained. Once again, I want to stress that the interpretation given below is rather subjective and based upon ideas foreign to pragmatic methods.

So, let us assume that the data presented tell us about the movements of the soul after death, and about responses of the body to its parting from soul. We can name this soul energy or spirit, we can guess which plane—astral, ether or air it belongs to, we can form the most exotic hypotheses of its nature—at this stage it does not play a significant role. The main point is that we accept this assumption and try to look at the material presented from this point of view.

In the cases of a calm, 'senile' death, the life-cycle of a person is naturally finished, he has ended his term, and his biological clock is showing midnight. The soul quietly leaves the unnecessary material shell and departs for further journey. But this does not take place at once: the soul remains with the body for two or three more days. It seems that this time is taken for some changes of the connections between the physical body and the ethereal one, some final alteration, the last crisis. One can imagine an analogy of the last inspection of a war fortress being vacated by the troops, when the vigilant commander passes along the already empty halls, where only recently everything was in a struggle, at work, in movement and where now one can only look around for the last time, smoke the last cigarette, turn off all the lights, and then move on to the new light, new life. From 16 to 55 hours after the death we see the oscillations of the curve that peaks upwards, as in experiment 2, or, on the contrary, tragically drops, as in experiment 6, but in any case in two-three days everything is over, never to repeat again...

The situation is absolutely different in the case of a natural, but to some degree unexpected death. In case 1 the thrombus could have dissolved, and the tragic outcome could have been circumvented had the man been more seriously concerned with his illness and taken the medicine in time. His life was not finished yet then, although who knows—maybe this life term was encoded in his genes and would have come to its end regardless of the thrombus that killed him.

But the soul does not want to part with body, she rushes about, as if again and again verifying the inevitability of the event. The Christian tradition always separated the cases of "unprepared" death. In the Middle Ages, death without confession was ranked high on the list of undesirable events: it hindered an easy passage of the soul through purgatory. In group I, death might as well have come suddenly, but all of the subjects were advanced in years and had inevitably been thinking about their last day, even without confession, and so they had been prepared.

The man in case 1 was in his prime, living in a socialist country as a simple worker—he was far from ideas of God and Eternity. All his life was devoted to a struggle for a piece of bread. Death came totally unexpected. Accordingly, we see on his chart (fig. 2.4-2.9) how strong the variations of his energy are. For two entire days—a long 48 hours—the energy protests restlessly until it becomes clear that there is no return. The last burst is followed by a sharp drop of the glow, as if some interior source is shut off. The ethereal body flies away, tearing up the last threads connecting it with the physical body. After this only an inanimate object remains that does not differ from the mineral world, changing and transforming according to the laws of chemistry. The tissues produces a smooth constant glow similar to rubber or plastic.

Now a tragic, agonizing, recognized death—the suicide in experiment 3 (fig. 2.15). The ethereal body is firmly connected with the physical body, the astral body—with the ethereal one. The totally unexpected end of life is a result of an accident, an evil concatenation of circumstances and misfortunes. Of course, on some deep level it is predetermined, but so far it has been possible to balance the scale somehow, to keep the hope going, to steer clear of the crisis, to wait for something else, to live on. But this time everything has become unbearable; this is the end point, the edge of darkness, the split where one movement can solve all problems. The tormented brain refuses to perceive reality and does not hear the desperate, but oh, so silent cries of the frail body, the body never listened to in the first place, and commands the hands to grab the rope. The stool is kicked out, and the delicately balanced course of physical processes called life is suddenly interrupted.

But not the ethereal life! This ethereal body is not prepared yet to leave the physical body, with which until a moment ago they struggled together through daily doubts. Maybe it is true that stronger emotions and experiences, more troubled feelings and sensations, more active participation of the soul in daily struggles tend to make more difficult for the soul to leave her earthly shell.

Then the soul lingers around, uncertain what to do, unable to be released forever, and so the glow doesn't settle down. Isn't this the reason for the Church's condemnation of suicide, as well as the prohibition to bury the victims on the holy ground inside the Church fence?. Wasn't the Church thereby banishing the restless spirit, which again and again returns to the body, troubling and frightening the living?

And, finally, the sudden death—a tragic accident striking down a person full of life, energy, plans and ideas. He steps down from the sidewalk in a hurry to cross the road a second earlier, and then a wild impact, flash of light, and the limp body is lying on the pavement, with life trickling out with the blood. Look at the curve of experiment 4 (fig. 2.17). There is a narrow thin peak in the first four hours after death and then a deep drop, in spite of the fact that it is the most active time, midnight. Photos of the glow clarify the reason for this peak: there are star-shaped, disparate spots, as if a set of snowflakes sprinkled around the finger—I have seen nothing similar in my 15 years of experience with the Kirlian effect. It is as if a fountain of energy had burst out through the ruptured shell. It is quickly gone, but the connections are not severed yet, for the frail ethereal body needs more than a day to say good-bye to the physical body.

An interesting fact: in the case of a natural death by aging the process of departure takes a day or two; in case 4 one day passes from the end of energy fountain until the final rest. On many curves one observes a sharp drop after two days—is this a random coincidence or a manifestation of some law unknown to us, connecting life cycles with the most natural temporal periods affecting all living beings and determining the very course of all Earth processes: sunrise and sunset. But, according to our data, this period behaves as an absolute measure, not connected with the time of the day, and the end of the 48-hour period after death may fall on any time of day in most of our experiments. However, we emphasize once again that the present number of experiments is entirely insufficient for any final conclusions.

The tragic death of a young girl is represented in experiment 7 (fig. 2.23). The young, blooming creature has only just begun to live; she is only on the threshold of life, when all of a sudden such an absurd end comes. Had there been a different set of circumstances, had there been an experienced doctor nearby, she would have been back to normal in a half an hour, with only an unpleasant recollection of the event.

The problem of a sudden death, especially death of children and youths, is a very complex one. Here is what priest Peter Kalinovsky has to say on the topic: "A young creature's death would be not only unfair, but also senseless if it were the end of his existence. But there is nothing senseless in nature, and God's will is frequently unknown to us. A child dies sinless, and in the other world his soul should be happy. People of a simple natural life feel this. Such view is the most humane, and it allows the living to understand the event." But let us look at the curves of experiment 7. Sharp peaks, rises and drops, gradual downfall, but no wanted rest, no direct line. What does this curve resemble the most? Experiment 3, the excited energy curves of the person who violently ended his own life. Conclusions would be hasty at this point: one case is insufficient to cover this situation.

Another custom of Death is to claim the person who has had his or her fair share of good luck, fortune, success and happiness. The fare share seems to be different for different people at different periods in their lives. When you feel that you have had good luck too often or for too long, you must expect it to end—usually in a painful manner. Experienced drivers are well aware that small problems with the car avert a serious accident. Life is painted with zebra stripes: broad white stripes must have black stripes in between. The broader the white stripes, the broader and blacker are the black ones, with Death lying in ambush. Death expects to be paid 'the good luck toll.' Having it too good for too long is a bad omen. And many small misfortunes are much better than one great disaster.

In the 1980s there was a world-class climber in Leningrad[1]. I will call him Alexander T for the purposes of this story. He was notorious for having the fortune always on his side. Fine weather always settled in when he arrived at the mountains. If ever it started raining, it was not until he was safely back at the camp. His ascents were invariably *ne plus ultra*. Whenever he had to draw lots, his luck was flawless. He had an interesting job and a beautiful wife. One winter he took part in a 20-km cross-country ski race held at a suburban forest. The day was cold, and there were no spectators who usually crowded the hills along the race route. In the middle of the race, on a downhill run, Alexander fell and seriously twisted his foot. While waiting for help to arrive, he sat on the snow in his light skiing suit drenched with sweat. When he finally was brought to the hospital some time later, he was diagnosed with a critical case of pneumonia. He died two days later. While we are busy averting our thoughts away from Death, Death keeps an eye on each of us.

Another custom observed by Death is similar to the course of events above. The lives that are the brightest, most eventful and happy, most filled with achievements, with the strongest influence on others seem to attract the attention of Death the fastest. Suffice it to mention the Italian painter Raphael (1483-1520), the Russian poets Alexander Pushkin (1799-1837), Sergei Esenin (1895-1925), Vladimir Vysotski (1938-1980), the English poet George Gordon Byron (1788-1824). Their lives flashed like bright comets. Brimming over with high spirits, each of them lived a life filled with great deeds, great achievements,

1    *Now renamed St. Petersburg*

and great passions that would more than fill a few average lives! Thousands of lives orbited around theirs, were influenced by them or depended on them and their actions. Incidentally, let us ask ourselves, what professions render their practitioners most influential and magnetic? The answer is simple: authors and politicians (though, of course, not any writer or any man in the corridors of power would qualify for this definition). Oddly, these are the two professions particularly attractive to Death. A list of authors who died young may be found in any literature textbook.

Politicians are worthy of a special mention. In the *Encyclopedia of Death*, an unusual book by Alexander Lavrin, the profession of the *Head of State* (Monarch, President, Prime Minister) is listed as the most dangerous with respect to the ratio of those assassinated to the total number of rulers. There are 55 names on the incomplete list of the 20th- century heads of different states in the world. The compiler of the Encyclopedia of Death gives the names of prominent politicians only, e.g. the Indian Prime Ministers Indira Gandhi and Rajiv Gandhi, the US Presidents William McKinley and John F. Kennedy, the Chilean President Salvador Aliende, the Swedish Prime Minister Olaf Palme, the Italian dictator Benito Mussolini, the Romanian ruler Nicolae Ciauchescu. The 20th-century situation has been quite consistent with all preceding centuries. If we were to cite the rulers and monarchs murdered in olden times, volumes would have to be written to include all their names. For example, out of fifty Russian Grand Dukes and Czars ruling in succession from the tenth century to 1917, fourteen have been murdered—that's a mortality rate of 28%. There is no other profession, trade, or occupation in this country with such a heavy toll.

I should think that in this particular respect the history of any other country is rather similar to that of Russia. Shakespeare summed it up as follows,

*For God's sake, let us sit upon the ground*
*And tell sad stories of the dead kings:*
*How some have been deposed, some slain in war,*
*Some hounded by the ghosts they have deposed;*
*All murdered: for within the hollow crown*
*That rounds the mortal temples of a king*
*Keeps Death his court ...*
*(Richard II; III, ii)*

A detailed study of instances of assassination yields some curious data, with striking coincidences. I will cite the lives of two outstanding American politicians: Abraham Lincoln, elected senator in 1847, elected president in

1860; and John F. Kennedy, elected senator in 1947, elected president in 1960. Each married a bride of age 24. President Lincoln had a secretary named Kennedy; president Kennedy had a secretary named Lincoln. Both presidents were succeeded by a Johnson after assassination: Andrew Johnson, the 17th President, and Lyndon Baines Johnson, the 36th President. The two Johnsons were born in 1808 and 1908, respectively. Both Lincoln and Kennedy had premonitions of approaching mortal danger. Both of their assassins were killed shortly after they committed the crime. The chain of coincidences is extraordinary.

Statesmen of other ranks appear to be in great danger, too. The Swiss historian Felix Auer suggests that in the course of European history, the post of Minister of Finance has often been a favorite with Death: 37 French ministers of finance suffered a martyr's death from 1315 to 1781. It may be concluded that the more powerful the person and the higher his position in society, the more effectively he secures the attention of Death.

On the other hand, Death seems to be in no hurry when someone has a set purpose and is striving to achieve a goal in life. Such a person is usually allowed to attain the goal, and immediately afterwards Death arrives to claim the toll. This appears to be especially true of those who would take arms against a vast sea of trouble. Old age was granted to those politicians who strove to establish great empires and managed to reach the summit of power only after many years of struggle—Tatar's Genghiz Khan, Asia's Tamerlane, Japan's Tototomi Hideyoshi; as well as to philosophers who founded great religions—Moses, Mohammed, Confucius, Chang Tao-Ling; and to those who devoted their lives to reflection, meditation and creative work—monks, scholars, great authors. With respect to the above category of politicians, prophets etc., longevity is not correlated with the intensity of their lives. Many a person from the high-longevity group has had a tempestuous and eventful life, and has often been in danger of losing life. Each, however, had been striving for a great goal which was eventually attained.

# Our Sensations

The question that was raised in the very beginning of our experiments was: what is the meaning of increased overnight activity? We observed this phenomenon on the first experimental night. In the morning, the night-shift experimenter, a regular employee of the organization, noted a few things:

*"Throughout the night I felt the presence of a substance. "*
*"What's that,"—I asked, not understanding him.—"Presence of what?*

*"Substance. So we call the meandering spirit of the dead man. Everyone who works in our institution for a while, if they do not become drunkards, begin to feel it in due course. At nights and on weekends it is usually much stronger than by day. And this night particularly, the substance was felt especially clearly.*

*In the beginning of the experiment I went down to the basement hourly, and routinely conducted the photographic work. I have worked in this institution for a few years and have seen a lot. At 11:45 p.m., as usual, I entered the basement and came to the body. Suddenly I was shocked by a strong sensation of fear, entirely wild, my hair stood on end. As I recalled later I had felt such panic only once before, during a bear hunt: we were tracking the animal, when all of a sudden I had a gut feeling that the bear was actually behind me, and did not harbor peaceful intentions. Now I was gripped by the same primal fear. I tried to calm myself, but in vain—the fear did not subside. I took the photo quickly and almost ran out upstairs. Isn't it funny? A strong man, a professional, a hunter—and afraid of ghosts! But I did not want to go back to the body unnecessarily. These sensations recurred all night until 5 a.m., though, of course not with such intensity when I was prepared to face them. But when I entered the basement at 6 a.m., everything was quiet again.*

*Later on, I tried to understand, what had happened to me? This fear could not be subdued by logic, as if my subconsciousness had felt the danger and reacted to it in a primal way. A very interesting and new sensation!"*

I wondered how the next night would go.

On the next night the sensation was repeated only once, at 3 a.m.; on the third night there was absolutely nothing. In the second experiment my assistants have had no unpleasant sensations. That is why, naturally, I decided to check everything myself in the following experiment. Coincidentally it was experiment 3—a suicide case.

It is 11:45 at night. I come from the laboratory and along the deserted staircase, down to the basement. It is absolutely quiet in the building. Somewhere in distant rooms there are guards and my colleagues. I am alone. The halls and the operating rooms are unusually empty. In the daytime, I would see gurneys with dead bodies each step of the way, just brought in or being prepared for autopsy. At night they are all moved to the freezers. Rarely does one see a body brought in at night.

Passing by the morgue, I come down still lower to the basement, and along the concrete corridor to the door of our experimental room. Even in the daytime, the main denizens down here are rats. I unlock a small iron door, having some difficulty using the keys in the dim light of a bulb. After this dim light I usually stand still for some time to allow my eyes to get accustomed to the red semidarkness of the basement. I stand and appraise my sensations. Throughout the many years of research with others who have extra-sense capacity, I had gone through numerous training sessions that develop sensitivity and the ability to perceive fragile energies. The skills thus acquired have been rather useful in everyday life. Therefore I pull myself together and try to perceive what I can.

I feel nothing but an empty room. The subject is at the distant end from the door, about 20 meters away. I begin to move slowly ahead. I reach the middle of the basement when suddenly I feel someone's glance directed at me. Everyone has experienced this sensation, the pressure of someone's gaze on your back in a crowd, a store, or a bus. But in a crowd, you can turn and meet the eyes of the 'intruder' who is the source of this nuisance. Here, in the middle of the basement, of course, I can find no such source. The basement is empty, and the entire building contains no more than five people. But the presence is felt very succinctly. I come to the subject and turn on the equipment. The sensation is that someone is lingering nearby, watching all my actions. There is no hostility in this presence, only quiet observation. *Quiet*, but not *indifferent*.

I get the sensation that this observer is here by right, while I am here by accident and for no reason. In the evening before the beginning of my shift I was going to stay in the basement for the hour that elapsed between measurements, but now this intention entirely unmotivated. It is not fear I feel, but rather the kind of discomfort you experience in unpleasant company: the sense that you're not wanted here. Finishing the measurements, I turn off the equipment and leisurely go back to the door. Here, the sensation of someone else's presence is absent. I once again slowly tour the room. Ah here it is again! I return to the distant end of the basement near the back wall, about three meters from the gurney with the body. Here the sensation is present but not strongly. Eventually I manage to determine that the presence is most intense approximately in the center of the room, some 5-7 meters from the body. Then I decide that I can scarcely do more, and I head for the exit. This time, I feel a gaze on my back until the very moment I exit. Only after closing the low iron door I realize how tired I got over these last 20 minutes.

Later on, all the members of my group of experimenters shared their impressions. On the whole, they rather coincide. The presence was felt especially strongly on the first night, though not in all experiments. As a rule, it was possible to detect a place in the room where the feeling was the strongest and this place never coincided with the position of the body; as a rule it was 3-5 meters away. Primal fear arose only in the first and fourth experiments with different operators. By daytime none of us felt anything, despite the same level of illumination in the room as at night, and despite our efforts to sense something. As the experiments progressed, we all became accustomed to these "substances," and were able to ignore them. At the same time, the presence of those sensations felt by different people, the inability to control it logically may testify their objectiveness.

The increased nocturnal activity is probably significant. Absence of activity in the day time cannot be attributed entirely to the of influence of daylight, or to the greater number of people present: our basement room had no windows and was kept at a darkened level of illumination around the clock; we also seldom entered the room with more than three people at a time. However, both the sensations and the experimental curves demonstrate increased nocturnal activity. Much more experimental data has to be accumulated before we can explain this phenomenon.

When I related this experience later at lectures, many in the audience were curious: why wasn't a medium invited to become acquainted with these 'beings' in more detail, and why wasn't there an attempt to make contact with these beings? The reasons have to do with my desire, at this stage in the experiment, to obtain more 'natural' results unaffected by any influence. First, the progression of the process must be observed and its features noted; then we can attempt to influence it. If mediums were involved at the very beginning, the very essence of the experiment and its results could have been altered unpredictably. Secondly, a medium could have become attached to the experimental room, exerting influence even after his or her shift. This could also lead to unexpected consequences. The reality of this danger has been proven through experience with gauges that register psychic pressure over distance.

In the future, it would unquestionably be interesting to involve a medium able to establish contact with the spirit of the deceased, and observe the effect on the outcome of the experiment. Naturally, these experiments must be performed with better accuracy, so as not to disturb the kingdom of the dead for nothing. These experiments require extensive specialized training and much courage.

Death demands to be treated with respect, with no mocking or unceremoniousness. This statement can again be illustrated by instances from the mountaineering practice. I attended the burial of many a young friend who had trifled Death, walking the razor's edge. I found out that the second and third years of rock climbing prove to be the most dangerous for a sportsman: the climber has been trained, has had several successful climbs, and is beginning to think that every mountain is attainable. The lure of the mountains and the promise of the champion's spoils has made many a sportsman think of competition rather than of one's safety. It is then that the climber usually gets into trouble. Naturally, those who survive will change their attitude towards danger radically.

Though it had a happy ending, my personal crisis of that kind left me brimming over with emotions. One spring, on the eve of the climbing season, my friend and I went for a rock climb in the country. We were going to do training climbs up a wall, with safety provided from below. This usually means that one sportsman, with the end of the rope tied to his harness, climbs up, hammering pitons into the cracks and pulling the rope through the carabiners attached to the pitons, while the partner stays below, holding the other end of the rope. I had climbed up about eight meters and had hammered in two pitons, when I was stopped by an overhang. I groped my way around, trying to find a grip, or a suitable crack for the piton to be driven in, but I found neither. Later, I learned that in this situation the only reasonable way out is to descend, examine the rock wall once again, and see what can be done about it from the bottom. As a rule, a way out can always be found. On that spring day I did not descend. I wanted to climb up at all costs. After some groping, I found what I thought was a thin crack, into which I inserted a light "petal" peg, hung a light rope ladder over it, and stepped onto the lowest rung. I was going to move upwards in search of a shelf, but the peg shot out and I fell, back first, from the height of a three-story building, pulling out all the pitons that I had driven in minutes earlier... When I regained consciousness, I was told to lie still for a half an hour. Then my friend helped me up, and I was even able to waddle to the bus. My whole body was in pain. An X-ray examination made at the nearest emergency center showed no fractures, and I was allowed to go home.

At midnight, in bed, I suddenly felt the breath of Death. Pain attacked me in waves, and each new wave seemed more and more unbearable. Breathing was painful too. When I tried to hold my breath and take a deep breath afterwards, it resulted in a sharp pang. A veil hung before my eyes. I felt like I was dying. The pain was so severe that there was no room for any coherent thoughts, fear, or remorse. I was only able to wake up my wife and ask her to call for an ambulance. My state of mind could be described as a total absence of mind. I only wanted the pain to be over. I did not care what the outcome would be or in what manner it would be reached. I had no other wish or thought. Once I was brought to the hospital I received some injections, put to bed, and in the morning I felt I was to live on...

After the incident it took me a long year of training to overcome the fear of another fall and to be able to climb in the mountains effectively and professionally. From then on, I was able to have every situation under control. I did my job carefully and, at the same time, quickly and energetically. For many years after the incident, I went to the mountains as a group leader, I happened to get into various kinds of trouble, but my recollection of the past always helped me keep the presence of mind.

The long happy months spent in the mountains with daring and fearless people and my regular work with rescue parties led me to another conclusion—Death is rather partial in his treatment of people. Some are allowed to be rescued, and others are done away with mercilessly. I shall never forget an incident, or accident, that occurred at the Shkhelda Mountaineering Camp in Central Caucuses. A very young girl slipped on the path. She fell down and rolled some four meters down a slant. At the end of her fall, her head struck a rock. The shock was so violent that she died of internal hemorrhaging on the way to the hospital.

I will give another example. There is a climbers' club in St. Petersburg, which suffers from a reputation of regular, frequent accidents. The climbers in the club are all very young, and the instructors are inclined to believe that the accidents may have been caused by the climbers' lack of experience. Try as they could, they could do nothing to improve the situation. Death keeps visiting the club at regular intervals. I believe that it is the general atmosphere of recklessness reigning at the club that causes the frequent accidents. Heedless of danger, they keep climbing in the hope that they will have good luck. On the whole, one would think that Death likes people to be brave and reckless. Testing them, Death lets them have more and more opportunities. The difficult problem is to find an equilibrium, to try and keep within the bounds of bravery. You go beyond those bounds, and you are impudent, which must be punished.

There is a Serenity prayer that says, in one of its variations:

*"God grant me the serenity*
*To accept the things I can not change,*
*Courage to change the things I can,*
*And the wisdom to know the difference..."*

It reminds me of a Chinese parable. Young pupils asked their wise old master, how to behave so as to avoid all the traps set by life, and to be able to reach a respectable old age. The master answered by telling them the story of a traveler who had to cross a rapid river. All depends on the choices you make:

*"One traveler may aim at crossing to a place up the river. He will have to swim hard so as to avoid being swept away by the current. He may be able to conquer the stream and be eventually satisfied with his performance. Although content, he will be in a state of utter exhaustion after crossing the river. On the other hand, he may be overpowered by the stream, thrown against a rock and get killed. A wiser traveler will choose to cross to a place down the river. Then he will swim with the stream, and will only have to direct his course a little. Feeling much refreshed, he will continue his way on land happily."*

Every human being can be compared with either of the travelers in the parable. In the turbulent flow of life, some struggle *against* the current, trying to ignore the natural elements, while others flow *with* the stream of life. The latter enjoy going with the stream. For them, life is not an eternal struggle, but a pleasure.

There are no unsolvable problems for persons who live in harmony with the stream of life, because they set themselves attainable goals within the bounds of capabilities of their real world, and Fate gives them solutions, setting them on their way. The main problem is how to secure the awareness of the streams of life in the world, how to get a hold of the rhythm of the Universe, how to reach an agreement with the rhythm and keep pace with it.

The reader may wonder, how this discussion is related to the subject of the book, the theme of Death? I can assure the reader that the two are in immediate contact. Death is an event in the chain of Life. It is one of the numerous stations on the road of Life, differing from all the other ones in the fact that after that station the train of life enters a one-track tunnel, and we can only wonder what happens in the depth of the tunnel.

Our lives have been predestined by the supreme powers. The predestination, however, is flexible rather than absolute. Not every event or every date has been decreed. There is room for opportunities and probabilities. It looks as though a draft agenda is always prepared for every newborn baby, with correlations and alterations to be introduced later in the course of life, with personal variants, acts, and circumstances. I will call this doctrine "fatalism", but it is fatalism of a different kind from those manifestations of fatalism which were implied in the Greek tragedy or in Shakespearean "Macbeth". The terms of undetermined predestination are similar to the enigmatic statements in which prophecies used to be transmitted by priests at the shrine of Apollo at Delphi. This is the reason why we do not often think of death, although Death is always close behind each of us. This is also the reason why we avoid thinking of death, even though death is a natural part of life. In this respect, the human being may be compared to the butterfly which is born at sunrise and is to die at sunset. All day long, it flies merrily from flower to flower. Likewise, people enjoy the whirl of life filled with love and merriment, passions and torments, without ever thinking of the terminus. The process has been predestined. All our small, unreliable boats are being carried on by the stream of life. The art of life is to keep afloat, not to let your boat capsize in the turbulent flux of the stream, not to run aground, but to steer clear of the backwater from which the boat cannot be carried out by the current.

## Energy drain

I already mentioned earlier that 20 minutes of work in the experimental room strained my energy level drastically. As I found out, this was a constant: each visit to the facility was followed by feelings of tiredness and depletion, and each time I needed a rest to bring me back to norm. My assistants experienced the same effects. A significant drop in energy levels was also evidenced by Kirlian photographs, which we recorded on each other before and after the experimental shift.

What of the people who are habitually confronted with this environment, every day, week after week of steady work here? We measured their energy levels, taking gas-discharge photographs of doctors and aides. All three doctors who were examined exhibited normal images without anomaly, images of healthy people with slightly dissonant energy, light distinctions, variations and maladies. In contrast, all aides who were examined exhibited completely anomalous images—N-type according to Kirlian classification. They complained of numerous malaises typical of people with damaged energetics. To be fair, they were all heavy drinkers, so it was impossible to say whether the source of their malaises was work or recreation. Watching them, I recalled Mika Waltari's descriptions of the servants of the House of Death in "The Egyptian":

> *Priests directed everything inside the House of Death. Still, the minions, who took care of cleansing, preparing and mummifying*

*the bodies, were thieving all in sight with the righteousness of divine justification. Having once crossed the threshold of the House of Death, one rarely lost the stigma of disgust, shared with the entire caste, and was destined to remain among the corpses for the rest of his life. In the first few days, everyone seemed to me to be damned by the gods; their chatter, their curses, and their derision of the corpses disgusted me. Later, I discovered amongst them some genuine master craftsmen, who valued their skill highly and followed a certain hierarchy of superiority. Each was specialized in a certain area, much like the doctors in the House of Life, so that one was concerned with heads, another with abdomen, a third with the heart, a fourth with the lungs, preparing each part of the body for everlasting existence in the appropriate manner." (Waltari, 1993)*

As it happened, the subject of energy drain continued in a rather disturbing development. After the end of the experiment, we all became submerged in the worries of the summer : vacations, trips, or, as the case was for me, a deskful of experimental data to process. Not until September did I meet again with one of the physicians who headed the experimental group. He told me a disturbing tale.

A week after the end of the experiments, he was performing a routine autopsy. Carelessly, he brushed his hand against a fragment of the bone, but dismissed it as safe since there wasn't even a scratch on his hand. However, the next day his finger swelled up and began to ache; by evening he had a high fever, and when the ambulance brought him to the hospital, the diagnosis was clear: general blood poisoning. Only after two weeks of blood transfusions, cleansing, and medications could he go back to his normal lifestyle.

*"How could this happen to you,"—I asked,—"a professional for many years, how could you be so affected by our experiments?"*

*"In my daily work, I deal with corpses only for a short period during the day,"—he explained.—"The bulk of my work is paperwork, lab research, and preparation of documents and materials. In our experiments, on the other hand, we spent many hours each day with the bodies, including night-time hours, when the activity is especially strong. Although, naturally, there is also the end of the working year, accumulated fatigue, vitamin deficiency—a combination of factors led to a drop in the strength of my immune system and, consequently, an increased receptivity to infection. In the future experiments, be sure to watch experimenters' vitamin intake."*

It would be sad to find that the deceased actively drain energy from our live bodies. Rather, while existing in transitional state, they open a channel which connects our world with the world of another reality. This channel is where our energy goes, and when a person falls under the influence of this channel he is acted upon by powerful cosmic forces. He falls under the rule of laws and relationships that have a powerful effect on our lives, but are none the closer to our inspection or understanding. This problem will certainly require more attention in the future.

## Connection with Chakras

It would be very interesting at this point to discuss the connection of energy changes, represented by Kirlian pictures, with the activity of power-generating centers of the body—chakras. Chakra, from the Oriental point of view, is the meeting point of air force (+, yang) and ground force (-, yin) which meet at the level of the brain center (Brahman window). Air and ground forces unite at embryo conception and give rise to fetal growth. These forces depend on the consumed yin and yang products.

Chakra system consists of seven chakras which are normally depicted as a sort of "spinal column" with three channels which interweave, the crossing points being the sites of the chakras. These three channels are called *sushumna*, which seems to be analogous to the central nervous system; ida; and pingala, which links with the parasympathetic nervous system.

The root chakra (Muladhara), Fig. 1.2, is situated at the end of the tail bone in the perineum, and together with the second chakra (Swadhistana), located at the root of the spinal cord, are linked with certain aspects of uro-genital system. The third chakra (Manipura) is located behind the navel and is linked with the solar plexus. The fourth chakra (Anahata) is located behind the heart and is linked with the cardiac plexus. The fifth chakra (Vishuddha) is located in the neck and is linked with the throat. The sixth chakra (Ajna) is located in the head, and in accordance with modern ideas, is connected with pineal gland [Davidson, 1988; Roney-Dougal, 1993]. The seventh chakra (Sahasrara) is at the crown of the head. These chakras are considered to be energy nodes linking the physical with the spiritual.

At the same time we have clear ideas on the correspondence between different fingers and organism's zones. Though it will be discussed in more detail in chapter 2, here is an outline of the principal correlations:

thumb . . . . . . . . head-throat zone;

fore finger . . . . . . spine zone, large intestine;

middle finger . . . . . abdominal zone, blood circulation;

ring finger . . . . . . sexual domain;

little finger . . . . . . heart zone

To these zones one might attribute the chakras arranged in the given areas, that creates the following correlation:

thumb . . . . . . . . . . Ajna - Vishuddha Chakra;

fore finger . . . . . . . . Manipura Chakra;

middle finger . . . . . . Muladhara - Swadhistana Chakra;

ring finger . . . . . . . Swadhistana - Muladhara Chakra;

little finger . . . . . . . Anahata Chakra

This division correlates very well with ideas of Korean Professor Park Jae Woo, founder of Su Jok acupuncture system [Park Jae Woo, 1993]. In accordance with his ideas, the palm of a hand may be seen as a representation of a whole body (fig, 1.3) and both diagnostic and treatment may be done through the palm. Professor Park and his colleagues developed a set of techniques that is widely used all over the world. This, for example, clearly shows why Anahata Chakra is correlated with Little finger. So we may see on the fingers representation of all the chakras, without the crown chakra, Sahasrara, located above the head. If one places the Kirlian pictures of the fingers in a row, as is usual for diagnostic purposes (fig. 1.4), it can be seen that in this case chakras need to be connected not with a whole glow, but with some its parts. These ideas are to be discussed in more detailed in our book on Kirlian Aura. The points of the tips of chakras, where they are connected to the main power current, are called the roots or the hearts of the chakras. Within these hearts there are seals which control exchange of energy between layers of the aura through that chakra. That is, each of the seven chakras has seven layers, each corresponding to a layer of the auric

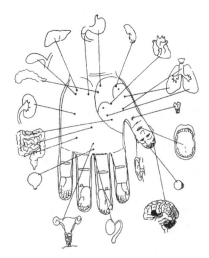

*Fig. 1.3. Correlation between the palm and the whole body after Prof. Park Jae Woo.*

field. Each chakra looks different on each of these layers. For certain energy to flow from one layer to another through the chakra it must pass through the seals in the roots of the chakras. Fig. 1.5 shows the auric field with all seven interpenetrating layers, and all seven interpenetrating layers of chakras.

Energy can flow into all of these chakras from the Universal Energy Field. Each swirling vortex of energy appears to suck or enter energy from the UEF. They appear to function as fluid vortices we are familiar with in water or in air such as whirlpools, cyclones, water spouts and hurricanes. The open end of a normal chakra in the first layer of the aura is about six inches in diameter at a distance of one inch from the body. Each of these vortices exchanges energy with the UEF. Thus, when we speak of feeling "open", that is literally true. All the chakras and acupuncture points are openings for energy to flow into and out of the aura. We are like sponges in the energy sea around us. Therefore, we can see that staying "open" means two things. First, it means metabolizing a lot of energy from the universal field through all the chakras. Second, it means letting in, and in some way dealing with, all the consciousness that is associated with the energy that is flowing through us. So the chakras of the auric body have three major functions:

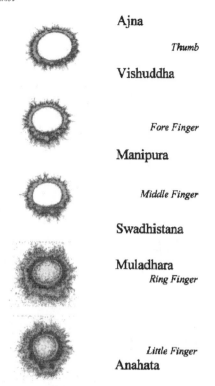

Ajna

*Thumb*

Vishuddha

*Fore Finger*

Manipura

*Middle Finger*

Swadhistana

Muladhara
*Ring Finger*

*Little Finger*
Anahata

Fig. 1.4. Correlation between Kirlian glow of the fingers of right hand and the Chakras.

1. To vitalize each auric body and, thus, the physical body.

2. To bring about the development of various aspects of self-consciousness.

3. To transmit energy between the auric levels. Each auric layer has its own set of seven chakras, each located in the same place on the physical body. Since each progressive layer exists in ever increasing octaves of frequency, this is possible. These chakras appear to be

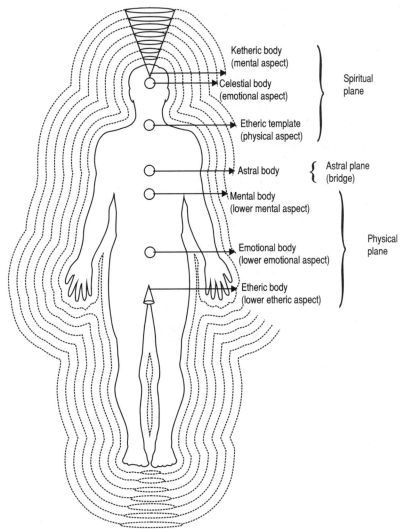

*Fig. 1.5. Schematic representation of the seven auric layers of the body*

nested within each other like nesting glasses. Each chakra on each higher layer extends out farther in the auric field (to the edge of each auric ladder) and is slightly broader than the one below it. Energy is transmitted from one layer to the next through passageways in the tips of the chakras.

In Oriental esoteric literature, each of the chakras is seen as having a certain number of petals. On closer investigation these petals appear to be small rotating vortices spinning at very high speed. Each vortex metabolizes an energy vibration that resonates at its particular spin frequency. The colors observed in each chakra are related to the frequency of energy being metabolized at its particular rate.

The process of death, which we would call transition to greater awareness, can be seen as a process in the energetic field. There is a washing of a field, there is a clearing, an opening of all the chakras. When you die, you are going to another dimension. There is *dissolution* in the three lower chakras. There is *dissolution* of the three lower bodies. When an individual dies, a trained person can see the opalescent quality of the hands, of the face, of the skin. It is opalescent mother of pearl as the individual is dying, and the beautiful opalescent clouds are wafting off. Those clouds are the lower energy bodies which serve to hold the physical body together. They are disintegrating, they waft off, and the chakras there are opened and there are cords of energy coming out. The upper chakras are great openings into other dimensions. This is the beginning stage of death where the energy field separates: the lower parts from the upper. Then, during the three hours or so after the hour of death, there is a washing of the body, a spiritual baptism where the energy is flushed through like a fountain right up the main vertical power current. A fountain of golden light flushes through, and all of the blocks are cleansed.

Does not this description correlate with the phenomena investigated by us? Bursts of energy, strongest in the first hours after death, energy fountain, opening of all chakras. This idea allows us to formulate the model of gas discharge visualization process as follows. Chakras for a living person are entrance channels of energy, accepting it from the Universal Energy Field. A healthy person has all chakras and he perceives Universe energy flows, feeding and energizing his spirit and body. This is represented on discharge photos as a smooth powerful glow. At the same time, this glow corresponds to the condition of the organism which has already accepted and processed this energy; therefore, discharge glow varies with a change in conditions. It characterizes the passing of energy from chakras along the channels. The same takes place with any biological object as it exchanges energy with surrounding space. Inanimate objects also absorb energy, but they only channel it, absorbing a part of it without changing it. There is total analogy with absorption of warmth which is really part of the Universal Energy Field. Structured objects such as crystals structure this energy near their surface, but this structuring is constant. In the process of illness, partial or total blocking of one chakra or another occurs. This results in energy blocking that causes the failures in discharge glow. We observed patients with a practical absence of glow. When chakras begin to operate in the opposite direction, that is they do not absorb but rather dump energy, it is followed by discharge glow bursts. But strong peaks at our curves were caused by exactly such bursts! Does this not confirm the idea that after death, energy leaves the body for some time as if flows away from it, and when the energy tank is empty the body begins to channel energy as any inanimate object.

However, the glow structure of this object corresponds to the energy of the body skeleton. Discharge glow displays the structure of an object as it displays the structure of a crystal or the inside structure of a dielectric. Therefore glow types for different groups are distinguished. But as compared to a living body glow, this glow remains constant from picture to picture without varying for a provocatively long time.

An interesting question: do discharge photos display particular features of the functioning of various chakras?

For a living person these features are the base of the Kirlian diagnostics. As was shown during analysis of experimental data, there is no particular difference between discharge curve parameters for different fingers. This may be interpreted as a practically synchronous change of energy in appropriate chakras. At the same time, small distinction are present, especially on the second and the third day of the experiment. These data can testify to delicate processes of energy redistribution, but to interpret it with greater accuracy requires a substantially greater volume of experimental data.

❖ ❖ ❖

The signs of Death are spelled out for those who have intuition, experience, and talent to read them. This capacity for foresight, or presentiment, is the highest level of such talent. Few people are endowed with this natural power, though some acquire it after an emotional crisis or physical trauma. The majority of those possessing this talent are not attentive to the warnings of Death. In the bustle of everyday life they just don't pay attention. It is very difficult to bring home the warning signs of Death.

There is a rock climber of high reputation in St. Petersburg, Guriy Chunovkin. Guriy was a winner of countless awards in Soviet Union mountain championships; his team conquered the most difficult slopes of Caucasus and Pamir. Once he was leading a team of climbers up a rather inaccessible icy peak face. The climbers had been working at it for three days when they found themselves on a small ledge, with an icefall hanging over them. They planned to spend another full day climbing this wall, and to have the mountain conquered by the end of the day. On the eve of that final day, Guriy awoke in the middle of the night to hear the water running down the canvas of their tent. He thought it was extraordinary: it should be snowing at such a high altitude, and no rain could possibly be expected. But the summer was too warm for any snow.

All of a sudden he had a premonition of the porous ice mass above them soaking up water and growing heavier every minute. He told us later that the warning had been like a blow struck by an invisible messenger. Immediately, he awoke his party to move down to the base of the slope. As they were half-awake, they obeyed. Then, the inevitable controversy arose from his decision: absolutely everyone was displeased, indignant, and scornful. They argued that they were so close to being awarded the champions' medals, but his egotism had deprived them of the victory. As I mentioned, Guriy is a man of high reputation, so four hours later they found themselves at the starting point of their ascent.

They left all pitons in the rock wall as they descended by the ropes. At seven they had a short rest for some tea and re-packing. They were going about their business on the moraine about five hundred meters away from the wall. Angry with their leader, they would not look at him. Suddenly they heard a horrific crash: the upper part of the ice wall broke off and slid down—very slowly at first, then gaining momentum. Guriy shouted, "Safety helmets on! Hit the ground!" They pressed themselves to the stones, seeking safety behind the boulders. In the next instant the gigantic ice mass crashed at the foot of the wall, with hard blocks of ice flying over their heads. A moment later all was quiet again. They had given Death the slip, but they did not seem to be fully aware of it yet.

The outcome will be quite different if you are not attentive to you own, or someone else's, intuition. I had a good friend, Kirill Varvashtian. He was clever, handsome, a favorite with women, and a fine mountaineer. In 1973 he was working as an instructor at the Dombai Mountaineering Camp in Central Caucuses. One day a friend asked Kirill to keep him company on a climb up the nearby mountain Bela-la-kaja. The rock face in question was not a difficult one for a first-class climber. Experienced mountaineers usually started on the route early in the morning to be back by tea-time in the afternoon. Kirill had no second thoughts about it. He gave his consent at once, just because a friend was in need of his assistance. The following morning they started very early, with light rucksacks on their backs. At the gate, however, a girl was waiting for them. She was a certain Lena who was very fond of Kirill. Lena rushed at them, begging of Kirill to back out of his promise. When asked to explain, Lena could only repeat endlessly, "I know that you must not go there today!"

After Kirill's refusal to oblige her (he thought it an absurd request, of course), Lena knelt before him: she implored, she wept, she promised she would do anything for him if he only stayed in the camp. By that time quite a few people had come up to wonder at the scene. Eventually Kirill pushed her out of his way and started on the path with his usual self-assurance. Six hours later he was dead. A slip on the wet moss sent him flying forward a mere three meters, with the resulting open fracture of hip bone. His wound was bandaged on the spot, a radio message brought a professional rescue team, but all was in vain. His shock ought to have been treated promptly, and his friend had no proper medication with him.

The above thoughts on the subject matter have been of general character. Do abstract theories help when Death claims someone you love? Can philosophy help if the person who dies is an integral part of your life?

Each of us is closely associated with many other people. The life of each of us may be said to be guided, if not quite ruled, by other people. This is true about various categories of people surrounding us: father and mother (who may be kind and loving, or alcoholics, or not known to their offsprings), teachers and instructors, lovers and spouses, children, and colleagues. All these people surround each one of us, forming the home, social and moral environments. All of a sudden a link in the surrounding environment passes away. When someone near and dear dies, this person is gone forever. It is a tragedy causing great grief. However, we can imagine that the person in question is gone to some end of the earth and is living in a place not only difficult to access but also without any means of communication. Incidentally, some ten years ago such a situation was typical of Russia. When a citizen of USSR emigrated to the United States or to Israel, hardly anyone heard from, or of, the emigrant. Correspondence was out of the question, since it might endanger the safety of other people. Those who stayed in the country were certain however that the emigrant was very much alive somewhere in this world, living his or her life. They also hoped that there was a possibility of their seeing one another again some day, through it might only happen in the remote future. Thus grief was reduced to sadness. I suggest that an analogy may be drawn between emigration and death, between making one's exit from life in the USSR and making one's exit off the stage of life. "*All the world's stage, And all the men and women merely players: They have their exits and their entrances...*" It is only the destination that is different.

With the analogy accepted, it should be easy to picture to yourself the departed alive. You can imagine that the two of you are really talking, because you know very well what kind of response would have been made if he or she had been alive. If you communicate with the late friend in this way, the deceased person will live on in your memory. As long as there is someone to think about the deceased, they remain with us in this world. In Ancient Greece, this doctrine was a religious belief: they believed that the soul of a human being will stay alive as long as the memory of the dead person was being kept alive. They had a tradition of commemorating everyone. That was why they erected their monuments and wrote their apices. Some historical figures—the ancient Egyptian pharaoh Tutankhamen or the Russian Peter the Great—may seem to us more alive than the postman whom we see daily.

A particle of Death exists in every human soul. Whenever a close friend or relation dies, a certain part of one's heart goes after the deceased, and the aching void is immediately taken up by the Death. The size of the part seized by Death will depend on the circumstances. When an aged mother loses her only child, she loses everything. Her life is over. She is still able to eat, and drink, and talk, but she is dead to the world, because she loved her son or daughter with all her heart, and she can never have another child to take up the void, so Death seized it all. When a Romeo loses his Juliet, the lover's heart is filled up with Death, too. In this case there may be more than one outcome. Overwhelmed by the sorrow, the lover may surrender himself to despair, and die. If he is not a man of impulse however his heart will be healed, because Death will be pushed out of his soul bit by bit—by other people, other emotions, other excitements. Distress and sorrow must be suffered, but they must be the emotions of life, rather than those of Death. Every person has one life to live here and now. One's life is one's own, and it must be regarded as the greatest happiness, a gift of God. Every human being has the right to enjoy every minute in this world with "the sweet keen smell, the sighing sound, the lights around..." All the other people in the world—the living and the dead alike—form an environment of one's own life.

The joy of life cannot be permanent, only the idiot is always joyous. In his progress with the stream of life, any normal person has to go with different waves—to be rolled by the mounting waves not towards good luck and joy, now towards bad luck and sorrow. *The web of our life is of a mingled jarn, good and ill together.* (Shakespeare, All's Well that Ends Well, IV, iii). If the progress is in harmony with the world and with one's own self, if he/she is able of forming a good judgment about one's age and station of life, with a sound mind in a sound body—then, and only then, moments of real happiness may be reasonably expected. What are the criteria of this kind of life? What are the reasons for expectation of happiness? Humankind received them all two thousand years ago, in the Sermon on the Mount (Matt.5:3-12). Whenever attempts were made to distort the principles of the sermon, or disobey them, the results were regrettable. All those who obeyed the commandments sincerely, and tried and lived their lives in accordance with the rules set up for them in the Sermon on the Mount, were able to be in harmony with the world, and ended this earthly life peacefully. The proof of the Sermon is in the bimillennial experience of humankind. It follows then that all other theses in the New Testament represent the Profound Esoteric Truth. Hence, why should we doubt the truth of the words spoken by Jesus Christ about entering the kingdom of heaven? The notion of life after death is all the more believable as it is similar to relevant theses in other religious teachings giving a warning of the Last Judgment. It should be noted however that Jesus did not spell out His answers to several questions that we cannot help asking ourselves,

- What happens to the soul immediately after death?
- How does the soul leave the body?
- Where does the soul stay pending the Judgment Day?

In the absence of definite indications, we can ponder over possible answers and make experiments. By seeking the Truth, we can find it bit by bit.

The above brings us back to the main subject of my work. It took me many years of reading, of thinking over what I read, of risking my life in the mountains, to be able to formulate my views on the subject of life and death, of existence and eternity. The next step was to go to the dissecting theater and see with my own eyes the human body without soul, the body that no longer contained a spirit. Eventually, I started making experiments which are discussed in this book.

Life and death go hand in hand. Death is brother to life. The profound laws and regulations of life are the same as those as of death, for in the face of eternity life and death are equal. When compared to the millennial periods flying by, the average seventy years of human life is but a tiny flash of light giving out a tiny sparkle. The sparkles are so many, however, that all together they produce a soft even glow—now glimmering, now blazing, but always radiant—which has been in existence these many thousand years. No sooner is the human baby born than it takes the very first step toward death. All the other steps are to be taken one at a time without thinking of the final one. It is only natural that it should be so. Absolutely all things and beings in the Universe are first born, then they grow and develop to live a full life, then they fade away and perish. The only difference between them is in the life-span: one millions of a second for the free electron, several days for the butterfly, years for the animal, millennia for the mountains, and millions of years for the star. As for extinction, they do not disappear—they get transformed. They all transfer into others forms and states: the electron is swallowed up by the molecule, the green leaf transforms into oil or coal, the star fades out to become energy. Even on that level, there is no death. Instead, there is matter rotation, a perpetual dance ring, a continual transformation of the kind of metamorphosis. The Universe is a unity. Each part of the Universe is in unity with all the other parts. Everything is transferable from one state into a different one. Everything undergoes continuous transformation. The human race is only a part of the process, a tiny grain in the whole creation, which has a place of its own—only we do not know yet where exactly this place is. Let us therefore be optimists. Let us believe that each of us will live a long and eventful life in this world. Let us believe that, after a life in this transitory world, we will continue living in the next world—and I sincerely wish a continuation of life to my readers, to my near and dear, and to myself.

# Conclusion

*Some people are seduced by earthly life,*
*Some, in dreams, approach the next.*
*Death is the Rubicon: no one before this wall*
*will know the Truth it hides.*
*Omar Hayam*

During the design and setup of this work, we were planning to see temporal variations of the glow images connected with the change of activity in the body after death. We expected that the glow of a dead body would sharply differ from a living person's glow, and I was not sure that we would be able to register it at all. However the very first experiment showed that at first sight there is no principal difference between these two glows. We were unable to discern any special glow characteristics inherent only to dead bodies. Types of glow images vary within a wide range, and transitions from one type to another take place. Glow intensity decreases as well, but not to zero, only to some fixed value. No specialist would have been able to distinguish *a priori* discharge photos of a living person from those of the dead. So, in one sense, the data obtained did not live up to our expectations, but far surpassed it in another sense.

We see as the most interesting result obtained here the discovery of the correlation between the *type* and *cause* of death and the character of the respective discharge characteristic. This may be interpreted to confirm experimentally the concept upheld by faiths of all ages and nations: that after-death existence is a continuation of earthly life and fate. Previously, these views, shared by most religions, teachings and philosophies have been either accepted or rejected, equally unconditionally. Their experimental verification has not been attempted for lack of adequate techniques and the need to filter some of the data through subjective human perception and recognition. The technique offered here and verified experimentally, entirely satisfies all modern scientific criteria: it produces reliable, objective, reproducible data that is absolutely independent of the experimenter's personality. All principles, as well as the design of experimental equipment, are based on concepts of the physical processes that result in the discharge glow; the apparatus was successfully tested in the process of patient diagnosis and treatment.

The second important conclusion seems to be the already mentioned lack of substantial difference between the glow of the dead and the living bodies. This may be interpreted as experimental proof of the absence of the basic boundary between the states of life and death; that is, as a proof of a gradual and smooth transition from one state to the other. This conclusion agrees well with numerous esoteric and mystical ideas, and suggests that after death, the frail body, or ethereal body, or soul departs gradually from the physical one. An entirely different question is how irreversible this process is—which moment is the point of no return, and exactly when is the last moment when these two substances—the physical body and the soul—are connected together? One might try to answer the latter question on the basis of our data, but the former question will require much searching

And, at last, it seems very interesting that even this modest set of data allowed us to single out some particular features and to serve as a basis for classification.

The three classified groups are: a *calm* death, a *harsh* death and an *unexpected* death. Of course, this classification is preliminary and can later be complemented and changed; however it demonstrates the *possibility* of such classification and, hence, the existence of some typical, nominal ways in which the soul departs from the physical body. It is possible that herein is carried the clue for understanding ancient esoteric texts, and the way to revise our current ideas about the human existence?

Additional verification is required of the found node points: the nocturnal hours near midnight, the end of the first and the second day after death. Do they reflect a common biological cycle connected with the solar activity, or do they have another meaning: why are they prominently displayed only in the cases of the third type, and in two others are either barely noticeable, or completely absent?

A fact that was established incontrovertibly as a result of conducted experiments is the absence of correlation between the fluctuations of atmospheric processes and the discharge characteristics. During the long period of experiments, weather and atmospheric conditions varied over a wide range, but their influence on discharge characteristics was not ever registered. This fact was particularly significant in validating the discharge visualization technique.

Naturally, all the data obtained should be considered as preliminary, initial steps on the topic. Subsequent experiments should develop it, and in some points, no doubt, contest our results. We see a large amount of work ahead, connected with finding new experimental data, checking the ideas and discovering new laws. Aside from this particular topic, a set of other interesting problems arise: investigation of the very moment of transition from the state of living to the state of death, revealing features and properties of this transition. Such data can provide new information for resuscitation specialists: it will draw the boundary line after which reversal of death becomes impossible. Another challenge—the influence of various illnesses, traumas, mental and emotional states before death on the process of transformation. This is only a small sample of questions which await being answered in the immediate and distant future. Analysis of our results transcends both biology and philosophy: it seems to me that we are standing at the threshold of a vast new world. The journey through it will bring us new knowledge and possibly a revision of many accepted notions.

# Part II

# Observations

# Introduction

This part of the book is devoted to the description of the formally scientific part of the work. In the first chapter, a short description of the physical-chemical bodily processes after the death are given; the second chapter is devoted to the technique of the experiment; the third chapter deals with Kirlian effect; in the fourth chapter the experimental data are presented, and the fifth chapter is devoted to discussing these results, all possible objections and arguments.

# Processes occurring to a physical body after death

*For the fate of the sons of men and
the fate of beasts is the same;
as one dies so dies the other.
Eccl.3.19.*

Over the centuries, different nations and civilizations practiced various customs designed to handle their dead. Ancient Egyptians mummified dead bodies and stored them in chambers, Hindus burned the bodies, Bushmen left them out for wild beasts to eat. Most nations, however, supplied their dead with all things necessary for continuation of earthly-type life and buried them in graves. They believed that future life in the next world depended on the handling of the body. But what does modern science tell us about the processes occurring to a body after death? What experimental characteristics have been obtained and what was their nature?

These questions are of basic value in the discussion of the data received because only from a comparison with these data can the importance and the meaning of the data received be clearly seen. Therefore, despite the specific character of the data submitted below, it seems to be unthinkable to skip this step. However, if the subsequent descriptions cause some unpleasant sensations for the reader, this chapter might be skipped and further conclusions taken on trust.

A huge volume of medical and forensic literature has been devoted to postmortal changes in body tissues. During the last 25-30 years alone, more than ten thousand papers and at least some ten books were devoted to the problems of death term diagnostics and various tissues outside the body preservation. Today many of these questions are the prerogative of *thanatology*, a science dealing with the problems of death and dying. This term comes from the name of the Greek god of death Thanatos, the son of the goddess Hekate and the brother of the god of sleep Hypnos. At the moment of death Thanatos flies to a dying person on his black wings and cuts off a strand of hair. After this there is only one way for the person: to Hades's underground vaults. We shall not survey the literature in detail, referring only to some books and giving a short review. [Polson, 1985. Simpson, 1952]

In a relatively short time after breath ceases (8 to 20 minutes according to various data) the cerebral cortex dies. This process is connected with dramatic changes occurring at the separate cellular levels. The cessation of substance exchange, connected first of all with the breath and blood current stoppage, results in inhibition of oxidation and restoration processes at a sub-cellular and molecular level. First of all the anoxia promotes the activation of catabolic processes in cells of the central nervous system. The oxidizing exchange type is replaced by the glycolitic type, which results in the sharp reduction of ATF synthesis and is followed by retarded electron transport, the infringement of ion gradients and the processes of free radical formation. The increase of cell membrane permeability results in destructive changes in cells. At first these phenomena in cells are reversible, but in the process of anoxia they pass a certain critical level and are transformed after developing irreversible degenerative changes. After this the destruction process goes only in one direction. Protein denaturation takes place in cells, which results in damage to cell structure and further in RNA and DNA disappearance. Autolisis comes next. The damage to different organs and tissues occurs at different time periods, depending strongly on the environmental conditions. At room temperature and a normal humidity for example, the marrow preserves up to 4 hours after the head stoppage, body tissues—skin, muscles, bones—to 20-24 hours.

All these internal processes are accompanied by external features. First of all the body temperature decreases. Temperature fall begins 45-60 minutes after death. This slowing down is caused not by the fact that after the death processes of exchange proceed for some time, but mainly by the fact that in the beginning the external layers are cool, while the inside layers remain warm. The body gradually cools down until its temperature reaches the temperature of the environment or even becomes 0,5-1°C lower due to the evaporation of moisture from the skin surface. The speed of the body temperature fall is influenced by various factors; under room conditions the body temperature drop follows some empirical laws.

One hour after death, the cooling of hands is appreciably felt, in 2-3 hours—face skin cooling. The temperature drop is on the average one degree an hour. After 6 hours the reduction of temperature is somewhat slowed down: 1°C in 1.5-2 hours. Total cooling comes in 24-30 hours. The dependence of rectal temperature change with time corresponds well to a smooth parabolic curve.

In 2-4 hours after death there appear corpse spots on soft tissues. Their development has three stages. Hypostasis stage lasts 4-16 hours; in this stage the corpse spot coloring entirely disappears after squeezing, as blood and lymph are moved from the vessels. The diffusion stage is 14-24 hours after death. The lymph and intercell liquid gradually diffuse through the blood vessels walls inwards, and dilute the blood plasma, which promotes erythrocytes haemolysis. Liquid part of blood also diffuses through the vessel walls and impregnates surrounding tissues.

Corpse spots after squeezing turn pale and gradually restore the color. The imbibition stage becomes advanced by the end of the first day. The liquid consisting of lymph intercell liquid and plasma impregnates the skin. Corpse spots do not change after squeezing. *Rigor mortis* advances 2-4 hours after the death. Skeletal muscles gradually begin to condense, which leads to their shortening. Total development of rigor mortis in all muscles groups is reached at the expiration of the day, and then the process of rigor mortis permission, that is muscle debility, begins. At room temperature debility usually is observed by the end of the second—beginning of the third day; at low temperatures rigor mortis is preserved for a more extended time.

Skin and external mucous membranes drying begins at once after the death, but visually it is displayed somewhat later. The so-called after-death hair and nail growth is caused by human skin drying and condensation. Initial rotting attributes at room temperature are observed on the 2-3rd day.

For the sake of a more exact formulation of "death" terms in forensic medicine, research of various physical-chemical body parameter dynamics were conducted. Among these the most reproducible were the recognition of the level of potassium and sodium content in intercell liquid, inorganic phosphorus, residual nitrogen and total albumin in blood and other body liquids. Electrical parameters of tissues were investigated as well: conductivity, both total and at acupuncture points, dielectric permeability at various frequencies. On the basis of extensive experimental data it was shown that all these parameter characteristics change smoothly, following the linear or parabolic dependence. For the early time periods, some hours after death, the registration of ultra-weak lightening of various tissues have been used the process being of smoothly decreasing nature.

In thanatological literature it is judged that knowing the cause of death (with blood loss or without, drawing, strangling etc.) and the environmental temperature, the application of a rational test complex permits us to establish the death rate of an adult person with the accuracy on the average from several minutes to several hours in 4-48 hours after the death period.

We report the data from the medical literature specifically in order to demonstrate to the reader the complex nature of tissue decomposition process and its inevitability. As the Bible says: "All comes in one place; all comes from dust and all returns to dust" (Eccl.3.20.). Therefore all tales about the rising dead and walking corpses are nothing more than late-night folklore. Appropriate physiological mechanisms of these phenomena do not exist.

At the same time, all literature reviewed with the description of experimental data testifies that in studying processes with periods more than three hours after the death no oscillating characteristic has been found. All the processes investigated were of smooth monotone nature. This fact is very important for our research and during further discussion of the experimental data obtained in the present work we shall pay special attention to this feature.

# ask statement: what did we hope to find out?

*Religion is the heart of an oppressed nation.*
*Religion is opium for the people.*
*K.Marx*

*If religion is taken away from the people*
*science can be served as opium.*

Analysis shows that all the data concerning "Life after Life" theme can be divided into three large groups:
- Data obtained in meditation, experience, contacts and hallucinations;
- Experimental data on the changes occurring to body tissues after death;
- Information on anomalous postmortal processes, increasingly obtained through non-traditional scientific means: parapsychology, transpersonal psychology, thanatology.

The first group of data is personal, being in principle non-reproducible, with the way of expression depending on the culture, age and race, but taken together these data tell a tale about some form of soul life after death, that is after the stoppage of the mechanism with which this soul was connected. Now we already know that the main part of this mechanism is connected with the soul only indirectly through consciousness: one might replace a heart, a kidney, attach artificial legs or mechanical lungs—a person will retain his own self. The big problem is to solve the secret of the brain: what is it—a subject or an object? A container of brain and soul or their only source? Shall we be able to keep the soul after a replacement of a part of the brain? Answers to these questions are likely to begin in the following century, but all teachings agree on the point that the soul can leave the body, exist outside it, perceive sensations, see other worlds and then come back into the body to continue the earthly existence.

Over the centuries these ideas marked a boundary line between two philosophic schools: Idealism and Materialism. For the followers of materialism all speculations about the soul always related to legends and fantasy, they explained this idea as the representation of human fear before the hostile nature, as their attempts to stand above the animal world. In any society poets and storytellers were appreciated and honored. And all religions were no more than canonized folk tales. Matter is primary, spirit is the generation of the same matter, product of brain activity, complicated structure, having new quality owing to a certain organization level. A computer comparable in complexity of its structure to the human brain in the near future will be able to compose verses independently, to make decisions and to demonstrate character. When a computer is turned off or when the brain is dead, everything is over—only matter exists!

At the present level of knowledge it is impossible to resolve this dispute. Neither party can give any unequivocal proof of their point of view. Libraries are filled with books, in ideological disputes fates broke and heads fell, but the question remains in the same state as in ancient Greece. But in spite of the fact that the followers of soul's existence have only verbal, non-reproducible, subjective data, this point of view is closer to us and in all further discussion we shall directly or obliquely use it. The second group of facts is a purely materialistic pathology—anatomic data about changes occurring to a human body mechanism after its activity stops. As an automobile left by its owner out of doors gradually rusts and crumbles, a body, left by the soul, shrinks and irreversibly comes to dust. Only the time parameters of the processes are different: for an automobile it is months or years, for a body—hours and days. This process is unidirectional and irreversible; when it passes a certain critical level the return to the former condition is already impossible, it can be only further destruction. All tales about living and walking zombies is a fantasy: as any mechanism, a body can function only in case of integrity and serviceability of the main parts and first of all of the General Managing and Coordinating Center—the Brain. But destruction in these tender structures takes place within hours. So the soul, if we are to acknowledge that it exists, after the death of the body should possess its own existence.

But there is one more question: how long does the soul appear to be connected with the body? Does it leave the body at once, at the moment of the heart stoppage or brain structure destruction, or does it proceed to come back to its dead shelter for some time in order to leave it forever at a proper moment? This question is not answered by autopsy research. Their task is to study the processes of *"...Decomposition of organic body leaving nothing but chemical components forming its substance... " (K. Marx).* And as we see from above, all the data obtained by thanatology testify to the process of a gradual change of body tissues with smooth transition from one stage, from one condition to another. Main attention is paid to revealing and researching attributes which distinguish the dead condition from the living one. It is connected with one of the main applied tasks of researches of this kind—the determination of the moment of irreversible transition from living state to dead and revelation of time periods and causes of death. *"Final diagnosis completes the autopsy,"* says an old medical proverb.

Now we may formulate the main question of the chapter: what is the task of experimental researches of postmortal condition and what do we hope to discover in conformity with all the submitted data?

We see the main task of after life state research as the search for objective reproducible proof of some characteristic bodily changes that can be connected with the transformations of spiritual substance of this body. As shown above, there is at present a large volume of subjective proof of separation of spirit and body; therefore, it would be logical to assume that the moment of separation should be reflected on the material body level, resulting in a change of some of its characteristics. Thus one can easily assume that this division is not instantaneous, that this is a process which takes a certain time, and follows certain laws and sequences.

Even from the medical point of view, at present it is impossible to determine for sure the moment of death (excluding the case of a serious mechanical damage to body tissues). What can one say about the bodies suspended in a functioning but unconscious state by means of an apparatus for an indefinitely long period? Practically all religions of all times and nations imply a more or less extended connection between soul and body. But what can be considered as an experimental proof of such connection? What body parameters should be investigated and what should one try to find out in these parameters?

The answer to this question is likely to be found in all the material presented above. Physical-chemical processes are gradual by nature, they cause relatively smooth changes of cells and tissue characteristics. Hence, rapid, non-monotone changes of these characteristics will attest to some dramatic bodily changes. This is a common feature of experimental science: variation of a curve testifies to some inner reconstruction of the investigated object. Experimental investigations of these changes should conform to all principal western scientific traditions: first and foremost they should be reproducible, at any rate in statistical data. Each object under research in the given experiment is absolutely individual and has its own behavior, but there should be some laws common for all objects. The following important condition is connected with this idea: independence and objectivity of experimental data. This means that results should not depend on changes of environmental conditions, equipment features, and experimenter's intentions. As a rule, any experiment inherits such dependence to some extent, explicit or hidden, and the experimenter's task is to find it and use some techniques to reduce its influence to a minimum. The opportunity of experimental repeatability of results in another place by another experimenter is connected with this condition as well. Modern science looks very cautiously upon non-reproducible data.

And, at last one more question: which characteristics of the processes, which parameters can reveal a response of material carrier to the movement of spiritual substance? It seems to us that it should be a set of parameters that demonstrate such a connection with the living state, that is, parameters that are correlated with the living nerve or psyche in a human organism. Hence, to find any changes of these processes characteristics after death, we can try to connect these changes with spiritual substance transformations, just as soon as we prove their independence from external conditions and purely biological processes.

In the present work we abstain from considering all possible processes of this kind: such task is for a larger research organization with better resources. We are going to restrict ourselves to the group of parameters most familiar to the author, connected with the process of gas discharge visualization well known under the name of "Kirlian effect".

# The Kirlian Effect

*From the fingers then the emanation activity
takes place. It is very important that
aura should end by network of living sparks.
Therefore even lilac and dark blue
auras should have ruby sparks in circle.*
Agni Yoga

## 1. Some Historical Notes.

More than a hundred years ago, a Russian researcher Nardkevitch-Jodko found that bringing any object to a Rumkorf induction coil or a Tesla generator caused a light blue glow to surround the object. The glow was produced around coins, leaves, ore samples and even parts of human body! One could not only see the blue glow, but could also photograph it without the use of a camera. These photos showed that the size and the brightness of the human body glow varies depending on the physical and psychological state of the subject. The discovery spurred much research and many publications. Physicians, theosophists, and occultists were interested in the results. In the St. Petersburg National Public Library even now one can read the book published in 1899 by the St. Petersburg physician Messira Pogorelsky "Electrophoto-photosphens and energography as a proof of physiological polar energy" (Pogorelski, 1899). A popular Russian magazine "Niva" published a large article about this glow. It seemed that the method would have an excellent future. But Clio the muse of history played a practical joke. 1914 was afoot, then 1917 and the research, together with the researchers themselves, were taken under rigid proletarian control. In these conditions no one could think of mystical phenomena any more... Many years passed and at the end of 1940 Semion Kirlian, a Russian foreman who repaired medical equipment, accidentally found this enigmatic glow. Being a skillful and inquisitive person, Semion Kirlian began to investigate this phenomenon and equipped a laboratory in his own flat, and in 25 years together with his wife Valentine developed a series of different devices enabling the sparkling glow of leaves, fingers, acupuncture points to be observed and photographed. At the very beginning of his work Kirlian was surprised to find that the electric crown around the fingers changes the color and size depending on the psycho-emotional condition. It was this feature of the glow that attracted the attention of scientists all around the world and caused a wave of publications and made the name of the Krasnodar inventor widely known. It is unimportant that later similar photos made at the end of the

19th century were found in old journals, that high frequency appeared not to be the main factor of receiving these pictures, that different modifications of the technique began to appear in various countries and each researcher tried to prove the originality of his own device—nevertheless, the name of Kirlian is associated with the sparkling auras and the term "Kirlian Aura" is known all over the world.

For the last 20 years of operation in the field of the Kirlian effect various researchers, the author of this book included, have received a lot of interesting results. We shall not draw the attention of the reader on the pages of this book to those results: interested readers can turn to our book *Kirlian Aura—20 years later* soon to be published. We present the main features, without which it is difficult to understand the sense of experiments described below.

First of all it concerns the nature of the glow. At one time the most fantastic hypotheses concerning the processes of glow formation were put forth: physiology energy expiration, bioplasma, Kundalini lightning and so forth. It required some years of hard work to formulate and prove the main ideas on the nature of glow formation and of object contribution to this process. Briefly, these ideas might be formulated as follows.

Around an object, placed in a special electrode system producing a high intensity electric field, there appears a gas discharge whose glow one may see and photograph. The discharge appears independently of the nature of the object; therefore, having a certain experimental skill one can cause practically any object to glow—a nail, a stone or a plant; any biological essence gives to this glow its own specific contribution, changing its brightness, size and color. So the discharge reveals features of an object that can't be determined with other techniques and allows one to track its small changes. Put a pinch of salt into candle flame—and you see its color change. Something similar takes place in our case. The electrical properties of the object, emission characteristics, gas production, energy exchange with environment—all these parameters of the object under certain conditions are displayed on the photos. For the complex object it is not always possible to distinguish the influence of one factor or another, that is, the method permits to reveal the complex organism reaction to different influences. All attempts to reduce the reasons of the glow to sweating or conductivity only, after careful verification appeared to be incorrect. Research showed that photographing is not the only method of the Kirlian glow registration. Valuable information is received during the measurement of integrated glow or the current rate enabling one to receive the data in real time mode. Fig.2.1 shows the block-diagram of the experiment statement with the use of a wide spectrum of modern facilities.

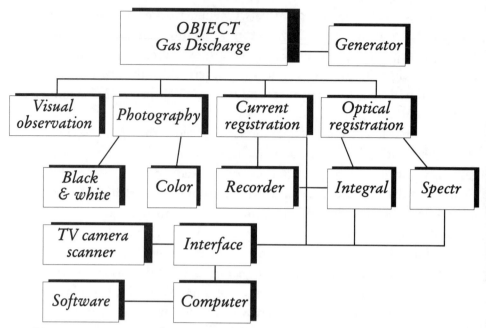

*Fig. 2.1. Experimental set-up used for Kirlian observations*

It was shown that there exist some types of the Kirlian glow that differ in their type of gas discharge. For scientific use a general term was suggested: *Gas Discharge Visualization technique (GDV)*, with two main types being: *Avalanche* and *Surface GDV*. For those who are interested we give a brief scientific description of the ideas presented above. This part can be omitted without damage.

## 2. Some basic concepts of the physical nature of "Kirlian Effect"

The first serious research of the effect showed that the development of the method is restrained by the absence of a definite concept of the nature of the images generated. Lots of ideas were proposed to the public based by their authors on a variety of effects from auto-electron emission to intrinsic biological energy. But all the hypotheses were of a purely speculative nature and were not substantiated by any experimental data. In the early eighties the Council for the Physical Electronics of the USSR Academy of Science presided by academician N.D. Devyatkov initiated a series of theoretical and experimental studies that helped formulate the basic concepts of the physical nature of image generation. Briefly, they can be summarized as follows. [Bankovski, 1986. Korotkov, 1995]

2.1. If a subject under research is introduced into a high intensity electric field then near the surface of this subject there appears a visually observable fluorescent gas discharge glow which causes the exposure of photo plates and films.

2.2. There are two types of gas discharges used today:

(1). A *sliding-type discharge* along the surface of a dielectric which generates images known as *Lichtenberg figures*;

(2). An *avalanche-type discharge* of the atmospheric pressure, developing in a narrow space limited on one or both sides by a dielectric.

2.3. In order to give a clear definition of the "Kirlian Effect" and to draw a line between the method being discussed and any other, which, though it might be similar is nonetheless unconnected with gas-discharge, it is necessary to introduce two terms: *gas-discharge visualization (GDV)* and *gas-discharge photography* which express the essence of the process of transforming the information of the subject into an optic or photographic image. The two above-mentioned types of GDV are *surface* and *avalanche* GDV, respectively.

2.4. Without dwelling upon the physical nature of the visualization process we shall pay attention to the main parameters of the subject that influences the character of the discharge and therefore of the image. These parameters are as follows:

2.4.1. The distribution of the electric field over the surface of the subject, as the subject makes one of the electrodes of the gas-discharge device; the non-uniform field may be due to the geometric or potential shape of the surface and if the subject is a dielectric, then the cause of the field non-uniformity lies in some incorporated defects and inclusions of the dielectric.

2.4.2. The emission from the surface of the subject: photo-emission, secondary photo-electron emission, exo-electron emission, auto-electron emission.

2.4.3. The changes in partial pressure and in the composition of the gaseous medium (consisting of particles and molecules) above the surface of the subject.

2.4.4. The fluorescence of the subject under the ultraviolet radiation of the discharge.

2.4.5. The perspiration, the forming of sweat-drops, the opening of the ducts and other processes which tend to change the conditions on the surface of the subject.

The peculiarity of the GDV method is that for most complex subjects it is impossible to distinguish the processes that take part in image formation. One can obtain only the general characteristics of the subject that depend on its integral condition and allows the dynamics of this condition to be observed.

## 3. The use of GDV methods for the research of biological subjects.

The principles stated above show a definite possibility for the "Kirlian Effect" to be employed in biological research. In order to evaluate its particular features it is reasonable to begin with some simple biological specimens which have such characteristics that are easily reproduced and controlled. [Korotkov, 1995]

Those specimens are microbiological culture and plants. It was shown that their discharge glow characteristic allow one to define the level of culture activity directly in the process of its growth, which permits to monitor the development of culture automatically and to determine the end of the process without any labor-consuming biological tests. Plant leaf glow changes in the presence of ecologically harmful substance, so the GDV technique permits to evaluate the plant reaction to a wide range of influencing factors, that is, to evaluate the complex ecological atmosphere in one place or another. In principle it is clear that near a brisk highway and in the depth of a park plants react differently to rain poisons, but to what degree? What will be more important—good living conditions or everyday training? What plants are the most sensitive to pollution? GDV method permits to answer similar questions.

Kirlian photos let one see the influence of plants on each other. Forest rangers know that no other tree can grow near the pine tree and pink flowers and roses cannot stand in the same vase. But these were only empirical facts. On a glow photo it is clearly seen that one plant's aura suppresses the aura of another plant, that its size and color changes if another more active plant is nearby. This is one more step to understanding the secrets of the Green Kingdom, the secrets of the earth. The problem of the so-called 'phanton leaf effect' is especially interesting [Proceedings, 1996]. But the most interesting and promising results are obtained from studying the discharge glow of human skin.

## 3. Results of GDV investigations of human activity.

Use of photoelectric methods of glow registration allows us to monitor the changes of human state directly in course of an activity: physical, intellectual or emotional. Typical organism reactions for various effects have been revealed and, respectively, the concept of norm and pathology have been obtained. Special experiments showed, that GDV method in combination with skin perspiration measurement permits to construct the *Selie curve*—organism's response to stress. So far this curve has been constructed only through the calculation of the blood particles number, for example, that of eozinofils. But this procedure is labor-intensive, and not very safe in the modern conditions—it is not pleasant to get blood analysis every other hour... In contrast, GDV technique permits to reveal stress phases on-line, and, respectively, to determine the operator, worker or sportsman tension level.

The Kirlian photography techniques have also been developed. The main obstacle for their introduction in practice was the absence of an adequate interpretation technique for the changes observable on displays. This problem was solved by the German doctor Peter Mandel. He assumed that the glow characteristics of human fingers reflect the level of energy of acupuncture channel, which initiate or end at the fingers. After investigating thousands of patients doctor Mandel developed diagnostic tables of finger and toe glow and offered a classification of the main phenomena. [Mandel, 1986]

Not all of Dr. Mandel's conclusions can be accepted unconditionally, but the main precept is certain—using Dr. Mandel's tables one can objectively analyze the physiology condition of a patient with all its danger zones in 10 minutes. Moreover, these photos permit us to evaluate the patient's energy level—an elusive factor, the basis of any eastern healing system.

The Kirlian photo shows to an experienced observer the distribution of energy in the organism and the type of this energy. In honor of the person, who made such a great contribution to the development of the method we offer to designate different types of discharge photos of fingers by the letters: K,R,L,N,S,D,V—the derivative of KiRLiaN Semion David Valentine.

Why is this grouping necessary? The work with *Mandel cards* showed their high diagnostic value and the possibility in most cases to evaluate the patient condition, in good correlation with other data. At the same time it became clear that similar evaluation is not possible for all types of glow: some aura types cannot be interpreted on the basis of Mandel cards. A physician should have an opportunity to reveal these types at first diagnostic stages, and at the same time to get some ideas about their features. The development of computer diagnostics system results in the necessity of allocating stable attributes for similar grouping. Dr. Mandel's classification in accordance with the photo view with the allocation of three types cannot satisfy us for the following reasons. First, from our practice, the necessity of allocating at least seven various types of displays becomes clear. Second, in Dr. Mandel's grouping there are no distinct classification attributes enabling one to relate the display to one type or another; and last, type names should not bear rigid sense attributes.

On the basis of our work we offer the following classification attributes:

- length and degree of branching of separate discharge tracks *streamers* in the crown;
- presence and percent of the total area of defects—glow phenomena;
- arrangement of crown streamers and their interconnections;
- contour presence inside the crown oval.

On the basis of these attributes the following classification was offered:

*K-type* bright smooth glow without large breakage and defects; streamers are long, branch-like, arranged close to each other, at the same time their structure clearly designates the contour inside the oval; the crown contour can be rough, frequently it consists of a dense inside crown and a more thin outside structure; the oval inside contour is clearly scheduled; defects not strong, not more than in one sector—less than 20% of total area.

*R-type* the same with defects from 20% until 50% of total area.

*L-type* defects more than 50%, but the inside contour is clearly traced.

*N-type* the crown consists of separate far-flung streamers arranged at a distance from each other, the inside oval contour scheduled clearly; in this type defects are relatively rare.

*S-type* crown consists of separate rare streamers or they are entirely absent; the inside oval contour is not scheduled.

*D-type* smooth crown consisting of separate short direct streamers, the inside oval is clearly scheduled; defects, as a rule not more than 20%.

*V-type* strong glow, close to K-type; the difference is that the streamers
are arranged so densely, that their structure is indistinguishable, the
glow as a continuous uniform crown.

The given classification can refer both to the picture on the whole and to the
glow in separate sectors. Using it for a variety of persons showed that to each of
these types can be attributed the certain psycho-physiological state, and thus
one can judge about the type of energy in each particular case.

Allocated types can be divided in three main groups describing certain
organism energy conditions. In the first group there are K,R,L types, in the
second N and S, in the third D and V types. Let us consider the attributes
inherent to each group.

Glows of the first group are characteristic of people with normal
energy, stable nervous system, in conformity with the eastern notions implying
a uniform distribution of energy along all channels. The power of personal
energy is determined by the crown size and defects and this attribute varies
characterizing short and long-term energy rhythms of the organism. Defects in
this type are steady and reproducible with 100% repeatability, although the
phenomena type can vary in different periods of time. An illness in such type is
clearly located, as a rule by one organ or system and the treatment can be
conducted in total conformity with western medical practices. For a person of
this group Dr. Mandel's diagnostics are entirely valid, which permits us to
monitor the course of treatment: as a rule, after the cycle of properly tested
therapy of an appropriate system the defects describing the given disease
process either disappear entirely or pass into a less pronounced form.

The second group of pictures indicates total or partial blocking of
energy; therefore Dr. Mandel's diagnostics in these cases can't be applied. The
state of patients in question is firstly characterized by the frustration of general
organism energy, that is displayed in the weakest spot either at the organ level
or endocrine or blood vessels level. As a rule such patients have diverse
complaints including total weakness, tiredness, sleep frustration, phantom
pains of arbitrary localization. For the treatment of such patients it is necessary
first of all to apply general therapy, resulting in the change of energy (glow)
type, that is, to transfer their energy type to the first group. This allows us to
locate the illness and to continue the teleological therapy.

At last the third crown type testifies specific condition of the organism
energy. At the given stage we can not define clearly with what processes this
type is connected, as it occurs relatively seldom, however as we shall see below,

D and V types were observed in a series of dead body glow cases, V type was observed during the aggravation of heavy pathological processes.

## How is Kirlian diagnosis made in modern conditions?

A patient puts his fingers and feet on a special electrode, a physician presses a button—and a blue glow arises around the fingers. Peter Mandel simultaneously received the photos of all fingers; in our technique we produce photos of fingers one by one. It is caused by the necessity of computer processing for a clear definition of finger axis. In our work we use special equipment designed to achieve a balance between the optimum information obtained and minimum effect on the investigated biological subject. The power generator supplies high-voltage pulses of 10 nanosecond duration following in short packs with different repetition frequency. Total exposure time for the subject is less than 0.001 second. As was shown by experiments, during this period of time the subject entirely preserves his condition—he has no time to react to the measuring pulse.

Our new Kirlian instruments, based on fiber optics and special TV cameras, enable us to input the picture of the glow directly into a computer. Once received, the pictures are displayed and processed by the evaluation of

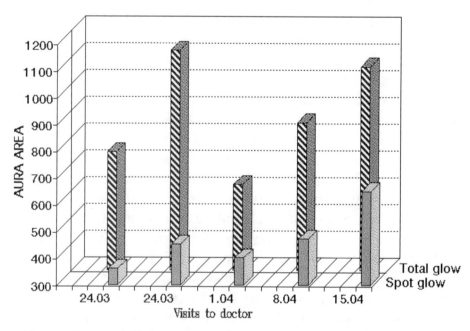

*Fig. 2.2 Personal discharge of a subject at various stages during treatment.*

total glow type and in some cases by the glow characteristics in various zones. The presence of defects in one zone or another signals some inflammatory process, the size of the defect characterizes the degree of inflammation. Computer processing of images permits us to evaluate the course of treatment quantitatively. Fig.2.2 presents the diagram of personal discharge parameters before the treatment, an hour after taking a special medicine and during three weeks in the course of the process of treatment. The diagram shows that the initial dose of medicine causes a sharp change of condition; some time later the medical effect vanishes but during long-term treatment the patient's condition gradually improves.

The detailed description of GDV technique seemed necessary because the principles used in investigating a living body can be applied to the dead body glow analysis. At present a large volume of experimental data on the evaluation of various factors which influence a living organism has been accumulated: homeopathic and allopathic medicine, alcohol, meditation (fig. 2.3), and alternative therapy. The accumulated knowledge permits us to get unique information on psycho-physiological states and condition of people.

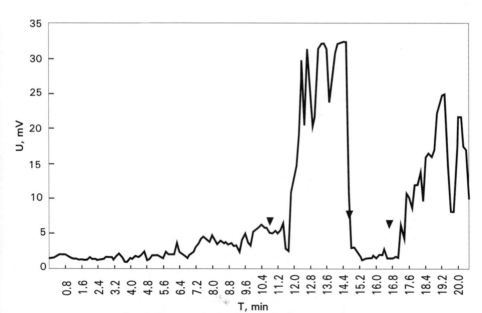

Fig. 2.3. Time dependence of the high-.frequency Kirlian current of a person's finger during meditation process. First ten minutes— relaxation, arrows mark the beginning, end and subsequent continuation of the meditation process.

# Research technique and data processing

*Well then, let us begin!*
*Without any hesitations I shall end*
*What have begun, leading to a nearest coast*
*The course of a tired ship.*
                    *Ovidi Nason "Love science"*

The scientific area we are entering by conducting the present research lies at the boundary between two well developed territories, possessing their laws and rules: the territory of the western scientific framework and the territory of mystical understanding. Development of the western and eastern sciences throughout the centuries follows different laws: western scientist investigated the environmental subject world, trying to touch, to weigh, to measure; wise men of the East have been meditating on the fundamental structure principles of the Universe. Everything, that does not directly influence the material world, that is, everything that cannot be recorded and measured, is treated by western science with mistrust and suspicion. The eastern tradition considers reflection and thought to be the highest step of knowledge. But the more advanced engineering and technology became and the more surprises they brought to mankind, the more often the West looked to the East, and the louder the voices of ancient wise men were heard. Western youth searches for an outcome in Krishnaism, Zen-Buddhism and Oriental war arts, scientists try to reveal the hidden sense of "Bagavatgita" and "China Book of Changes". The coming century promises a new step in the understanding of the Universe, a western rationalism and eastern mysticism synthesis stage. Therefore in the given work we tried on the one hand, to keep the stringent western scientific rules and on the other hand to take into account and respect the laws and rules of the spiritual world. At the present stage of knowledge we are standing at the new boundary, beyond which we can see vast spaces before us and can only guess what wonders and dangers are awaiting us there. We do not know for sure which factors are significant, and which are not, what will be important and what will be irrelevant. That is why while arranging and processing experimental data we took into consideration all possible factors which could in any way have influenced the experimental procedure and results, no matter how strange they might have seemed. Research to follow will no doubt show the meaning of different factors and results.

When preparing the experimental work we accepted the following organizational principles:

- reliability of data;
- objectivity, i.e. independence of the individual researcher;
- chance of independent reproduction of the results.

Let us consider the main experiment points and demonstrate how these principles come to practice.

## The procedure for obtaining experimental data.

All the experimental data presented below were received under the same conditions: on the same premises with the same equipment, operating in a certain stabilized mode with consistent technique. In the course of operation the equipment was tested and calibrated periodically. During the first seven experimental sessions on premises the constant temperature was +18°C; it was kept up by the ventilation and heating system. In May 1993 the weather in St. Petersburg was abnormally warm for our climate. The heating system was switched off and the temperature began to depend on the temperature of the environment, increasing up to +20°C by day and decreasing to +12°C at night. The humidity, atmospheric pressure and air electrical parameters corresponded to the environment. They are presented further in a description of experimental data.

The premises on which the experiments were conducted were a concrete basement 20 meters long and 4 meters wide. The subject under investigation was placed in the far end of the basement. After the subject was put into place, all equipment remained in a fixed position until the end of the experimental session. The windows were closed with dark curtains, the illumination was turned off except for a red lantern installed near the equipment. The basement was locked and besides the operators no one was to enter it.

All the experiments were conducted from Friday to Monday; that is, they covered three-four days. Twice it was possible to use holidays and increase the experimental cycle to six days. The subject for research was chosen on Friday depending on death conditions, age and sex. Each experiment, as will be shown below, required a huge expenditure, both in time and finance. therefore at this stage we had an opportunity to conduct a limited number of experiments and we tried to choose cases that ranged widely in their conditions. At the same time our opportunity were restricted by the cases that were carried to the given medical institute. In May when it was quite warm in St. Petersburg and a lot of people went to their summer houses on holidays the choice was sharply reduced. The selected subject was transported to the experimental room and was placed in a fixed position, head to the West, legs to the East. The left hand was placed in a fixed position on the electrode and was supported by a special device that provided the stationary position of the hand and the fingers during the experimental session. As was shown by the special measurements this system provided good hand stability, while not exerting any substantial pressure or compression that could affect the experimental results. The discharge characteristics of left-hand fingers were taken: fore, middle, ring and little fingers. The position of the body and the hand was determined not by any special requirements but by the arrangement of the equipment in the room, and in the course of all experiments was kept constant.

The choice of fingers was determined by the support system design. During the preparation of the experiment, the question of choosing the proper discharge characteristic was raised: as was shown in the previous section one might use photoelectric or photographic technique. We chose the latter for the following reasons: the primary experimental data are represented by a series of photos which are a documentary certificate, permitting us to produce different processing to get different sets of parameters; discharge photo technique is quite simple and practically independent of the level of operator's qualification and skill. So the photographic technique ensures both an increase in reliability and objectivity of data.

Black-and-white photo paper was used in all the experimental sessions. The data were recorded every hour during day and night. The working group consisted of 2-3 persons changing shifts every 8-10 hours.

The operators were to act as follows: once an hour to descend to the experimental room, to mark the photo paper sheet (date, time), to put the sheet under the fingers and to produce two discharge photos on one sheet, at the same time making the discharge photo of a reference mark, then place the exposed paper in a black envelope. Equipment was arranged in such a manner that to operate it one should only press the button. All the parameters were set beforehand and were held with accuracy of no less than 1%. 1-2 times a day all photos were processed using large canisters with—10 liters of freshly prepared photo solutions. After the end of the experiment the whole set of photos was taken for computer processing. Several times a day the discharge photos of operators' fingers were produced, which permitted us to monitor their condition. On Monday the experiment was usually finished and the body was handed over for autopsy examination.

So the experimental process consisted of three quasi-independent steps:

- the preparation, including the mounting and checking of the equipment, subject selection and installation;
- the experiment itself and draft material processing;
- computer processing of the experimental data.

Each of these steps was performed by a special team supervised and directed by the author.

Such process organization provided independence of the data from a particular operator's performance—his qualification, skill or knowledge. Subjective judgment was practically excluded. For experiments in the boundary area this is significant and should be taken into account.

For computer processing each photo was scanned in a certain mode, computer images were processed using specially developed software. This software operates as follows: the processed photo of one finger is entered in the menu and its name is indicated: fore, middle and so on; an operator sets an arbitrary point inside the photo contour, using this point the computer builds up an oval, correlating to the inside photo contour; after orienting oval axes the computer divides the image into sectors in conformity with Mandel cards, and calculates the following parameters in each sector: the glow area in three brightness gradations and total; the perimeter of the glow area, maximum image sizes. All these data are tabulated. Further, all tables are summarized in an electronic table that can be used for graphing. So for each finger we have a file of 5 parameters in 5-7 sectors for 70 or more hours—that is 2000 values for each finger or 8000 for the hand. The calculation of the area with preliminary binarization at a fixed brightness level was used as well. The results coincide qualitatively quite well.

As seen from the presented material, the research technique enabled us to obtain the most reliable and objective data. All the research steps were quasi-independent, the equipment stabilized and metrologically checked, data processing was supervised by the various operators, each of them performed only some of the operation. The technique of the experiment and data processing was highly automated and constructed as a set of certain algorithms that allowed to meet the above requirements. For example, using materials of the present book and having appropriate equipment and software one can receive very similar data.

# Experimental data analysis

*Carpe diem!—Seize the moment!*
*Memento mori!—Remember about Death!*
*Fiat veritas pereat vita!*
*Let truth be, let life be!*

As was noted in the previous chapter, the initial experimental data were presented in the form of gas-discharge glow photos of four fingers that were obtained every hour in two exposions to avoid random fluctuations. Computer processing allowed to get a set of parameters for every photo. They characterize the glow crown area in three brightness gradations. If necessary, these parameters can be used to obtain the information on the organism systems state in conformity with Mandel tables. In this experiment we needed integral glow changes during some periods of time, therefore of all parameters some were chosen that describe the glow crown picture completely: the total glow area, separate spots area, the glow diameter. In the first experiment description the curves for all these parameters are presented, for other cases—only some.

Special attention was given to the analysis of environmental conditions. In literature the problem of influence of atmospheric processes on biological systems behavior was discussed repeatedly and in some cases this influence was proven for sure. Therefore we found it necessary to analyze this factor with maximum accuracy. It is connected as well with our research method: gas discharge visualization. As was noted above the nature of pictures is determined by the processes of gas discharge development in the atmospheric air on surface of the subject under study. Therefore it would be quite logical to assume that atmospheric parameters can affect the processes of gas discharge development and hence the picture. This problem was repeatedly discussed in literature on the Kirlian effect but was not solved. Therefore our results may be of basic value. To get the most precise information on the atmospheric processes we applied to the most competent Petersburg organization in the field: The A.I.Voejkov Main Geophysical Observatory. Professor A.I.Borisenkov, the Observatory director kindly granted us all the necessary information on the days of experiments. After our consultation with meteorologists the following parameters of atmospheric processes have been selected for registration:

. *Electrical field E at surface level.* We think, this is one of the most important factors, as in some cases the external electrical field can be compared with electrode electric field and therefore can influence directly the process of discharge formation. The electric field was measured in the near-ground layer at the level of one meter from the ground surface. The variability range of electric field is rather high, it can vary from tens to thousands Volts per meter oscillating in value and sign during the day. In a good weather E = 100-120 V/m. So this rating is presented as a curve with hourly read-out for all the period of every experiment. For comparison with our experimental data this curve is presented in the same time scale as the experimental data.

- *Electrical conductivity of air N* is determined by the presence in the air of positive and negative ions, depending on meteorological conditions, season dust as well as some other factors, including the place where the measurements are conducted, positive and negative electrical conductivity can vary from unity to tens femtosiemens/meter. This factor can be very significant for gas discharge visualization as positive and negative ions can serve the berth centers for electron avalanches. Though the conditions at the Geophysical Observatory can be different from the conditions on the experimental premises and values of conductivity may differ, however the total tendency of changes associated with global processes in the atmosphere, will hold. All the more so because the Geophysical Observatory and the medical institution are not more than three kilometers from each other. Therefore we found it important to give the curves of air conductivity in comparison with our data. We pay special attention to the fact that for convenience of representation these data are given with the weight factor of 20.

- *The total ozone content.* Ozone is one of the main components of atmospheric gas. It absorbs the Sun radiation especially in the range of ultraviolet light. Total ozone contents is taken as ozone layer thickness in column of atmosphere of unit section at normal pressure (760 mm Hg.) and zero temperature. Usually it is about 3mm. As the variations of the ozone layer are not so large compared with other parameters of atmosphere, the ozone layer thickness variations are to be given in millimeters multiplied by 100 and such unit is to be named *Dobson Unit (D.U.).* This unit range is not very high so we give the subsequent values on experimental days only.

. *Total sun radiation* is the sum of direct and indirect sun radiation at a horizontal ground surface per day. This factor varies from units until tens MJ/m . The importance of this factor for biological subjects activity after the Chizevsky works does not cause doubt.

. *Relative Humidity.* It varies from units to 100% Substantial variation of this parameter can affect the process of gas discharge development.

. *The atmospheric pressure* is the weight of the air column above the point of supervision. For our latitude oscillations are in the 30-100 mm Hg range.

We might present much more environmental parameters affecting the experimental data, such, for example, as a moon phase, Sun spot intensity or star arrangement, but to avoid data redundancy we leave these opportunities for subsequent analysis and proceed to the discussion of the experimental data.

Further on for all the experiments the curves of E and N changes are given, all other parameters are presented with their average value for every day.

## Experiment N 1

The data were taken from 15:00 February 26 (4 hours after the death) until 12:00 March 1. The death occurred at 11:00 February 26. An automobile driver stopped at the crossing and died.

As was shown by autopsy conducted March 1, death was due to lung artery clot. Male, 56 years old.

Atmospheric conditions: low gradient field of increased pressure anticyclone, with its central part in western Europe. Atmospheric pressure 763/763/770 mm Hg on February 26, 27, 28 respectively. Ozone content 350/351/380 D.U. Total radiation 4.49/6.85/7.11 MJ/m2. Humidity 68/91/95% No atmosphere anomaly in these days was noted.

Let us consider this experiment's data in more detail. Fig 2.4 presents the curve of total glow area of the left-hand finger during three days after death. The asterisk (*) on the time axis marks the point corresponding to 24:00—midnight. As can be seen from this curve, during several hours after the start of experiment, parameter S keeps approximately constant, at 21:00 a sharp rise begins, which proceeds until 01:00, after that the S value returns to former rating. Practically one day after the death oscillations begin—rises and falls—occupying approximately 4 hours each, the maximum of these oscillations is reached on the following midnight. This process lasts approximately half a day more, exactly two days after the death the value of

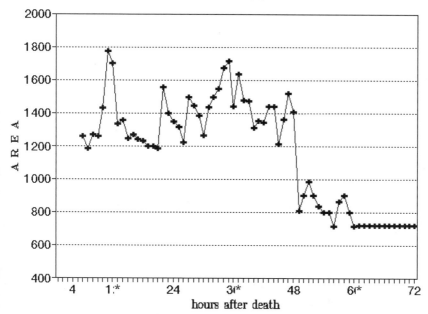

*Fig. 2.4 Time dependence of Kirlian glow area of a finger for experiment N1. The vertical axis represents the area of the image; horizontal axis is time in hours after death. Fore finger.*

parameter S sharply falls and with small oscillations reaches the minimum, kept until the end of the experiment process. We note the fact that on the third midnight no glow change was registered: it was smooth, weak and parameters were reproduced from photo to photo with an accuracy of about 5%.

These curves show a similar behavior with the other fingers. Appropriate curves are presented on Fig. 2.5-2.7 . The middle finger curve (Fig. 2.5) demonstrates rises on the first and the second midnight, drop in about 48 hours and a further relatively smooth process. The extreme peak reached at one experimental point can be connected both with the real relatively fast processes and with random fluctuations, which are indistinguishable in the given experimental session. Therefore one cannot say whether the single peak 61 hour after death (or 01:00) is important.

The curves corresponding to the ring (Fig. 2.6) and small (Fig. 2.7) fingers show the same behavior except the absence of an expressed peak on the second midnight. However the total oscillating nature of the process between 11 and 48 hours and the sharp drop in 48 hours is kept. Note that the small finger curve reaches an expressed maximum in 60 hours—on the third midnight. This maximum is represented by the three experimental points so it

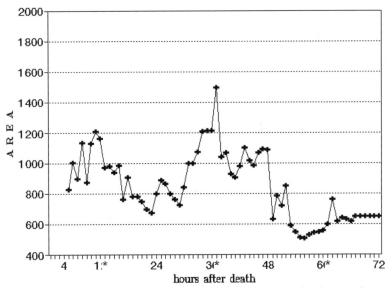

*Fig. 2.5 Time dependence of Kirlian glow area of a finger for experiment N1. Vertical axis represents the area of the image; horizontal axis representstime in hours after death. Middle finger.*

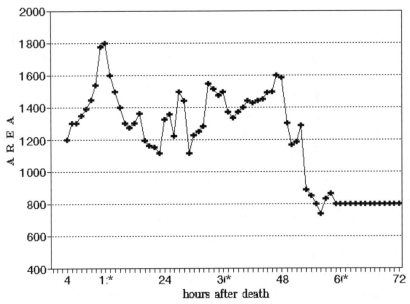

*Fig. 2.6 Time dependence of Kirlian glow area of a finger for experiment N1. Vertical axis represents the area of the picture; horizontal axis representstime in hours after death. Ring finger.*

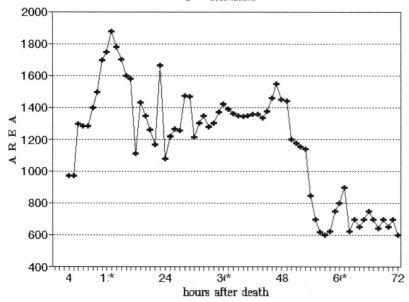

*Fig. 2.7 Time dependence of Kirlian glow area of a finger for experiment N1. Vertical axis represents the area of the image; horizontal axis representstime in hours after death. Little finger.*

takes place gradually during three hours period, therefore its position is quite definite.

A special test was made at this experimental session. We took the photos within 10-minute intervals during 2 hours, in order to test the validity of our experimental technique. These photos varied less than 10% from each other, which shows the validity of the technique.

The noted tendency was observed for other parameter curves. For example Fig. 2.8-2.10 presented the curves for the outside crown perimeter, the diameter along the main axis and separate spot square in the bottom segment area. All these curves have various degree of chaotic nature, maximum at perimeter curve (that is caused by the used mode of calculation of this parameter through calculation of the developed units number), extreme on the first and the second night as well are present but it is considerably shifted as compared with the curve of the area.

So the comparison of various finger parameters permits us to note two basic features:

- various parameters of different fingers have the same tendencies of variation, keeping the characteristic peculiarities of the observable process;

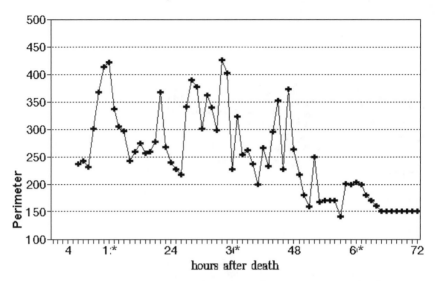

*Fig. 2.8 Time dependence of Kirlian glow perimeter of a finger for experiment N1. Vertical axis represents the total perimeter of the image; horizontal axis representstime in hours after death. Fore finger.*

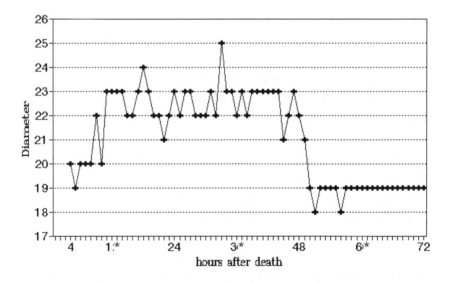

*Fig. 2.9 Time dependence of Kirlian glow diameter of a finger for experiment N1. Vertical axis represents the maximum diameter along the main axis of a finger; horizontal axis representstime in hours after death. Fore finger.*

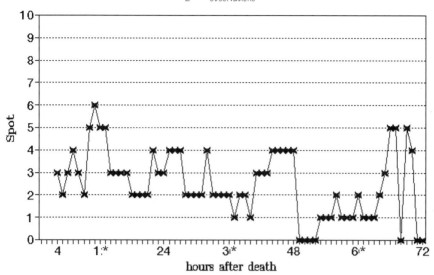

Fig. 2.10. Time dependence of a separate spot area of a Kirlian image of a finger for experiment N1. Vertical axis represents the are of the separate spot in the bottom segment of the image; horizontal axis represents time in hours after death. Middle finger.

- position and size of the most explicitly expressed curve extreme varies for different parameter curves; for example the area and perimeter curves maximum in the first night is explicitly expressed for all fingers although it has various width, the diameter curve rise is seen approximately from 22:00 and is kept almost constant for 48 hours with some peaks, but the spot curve maximum is observed from 6 until 11 hours (that corresponds to 22:00) after that comes a drop until 24 hours; although the maximum on the second night on this curve is shifted left to right.

These features show that an explicit hourly positioning of extremes is inadvisable at any rate of the given stage of the experiment. It is more important for us to fix the knot curve points. Therefore later on we shall not exhibit all the possible curves, but use only some.

Let us now compare the experimental curves with the electrical field and the number of particle curves (Fig.2.11). E-curve has two explicit maximums, none correlating with gas-discharge curves maximums. E and GDV curves have the same drop after 40 hours; however curve N in this time period rises, but as was mentioned above, the number of charged particles in the air can substantially influence the development of discharge process. So one can

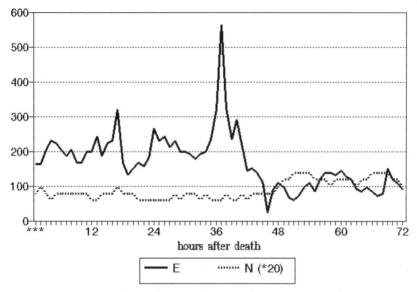

Fig. 2.11 Time dependence of atmospheric electrical parameters during experiment N1. E - amplitude of electrical field at surface level; N - electrical conductivity of air.

conclude that in this experimental session correlation between discharge parameters and atmospheric conditions was not found.

We can make the following conclusions based on the given data:

1. At the discharge parameters curves one might allocate the following characteristic areas:
   - sharp rise in the first night;
   - oscillatory nature of process from 12 until 47 hours after death;
   - implicitly expressed rise in the second night;
   - sharp drop in 48 hours;
   - small fluctuations from 48 until 60 hours—the third midnight;
   - constant smooth glow resembling the benchmark glow, though exceeding it by amplitude, after 60 hours.

2. Different fingers glow curves as well as various glow parameters clearly exhibit this area, though they are distinguished from each other by some features.

3. No correlation was found between meteorological parameters and discharge parameter curves.

# Experiment N 2

The data were taken from 16:00 (5 hours after death) March 5 until 11:00 March 9. An additional day off allowed us to conduct this experiment during 80 hours that gave us an opportunity to observe the behavior of the subject for a more extended period of time than usual. An old man died in the street at 11:00 on the 5th of March. A subsequent autopsy showed that he died of a heart attack. All the body tissues testified to a senile condition.

Atmospheric conditions: March 5 and 6 southeast periphery of a stationary cyclone with center above Scandinavia, March 7 and 8—low gradient field of increased pressure, March 9—cyclone back. Atmospheric pressure 762/766/777 mm. Hg., ozone content 328/318/339 D.U., summarized radiation 7.26/8.39/6.19 MJ/m2, humidity 70/55/92%. Schedules of electrical field and conductivity changes are presented on Fig.2.12. It is clear from the presented data and especially from Fig.2.12 curves, atmospheric processes on those days were unstable: practically all parameters show substantial oscillations.

Fig.2.13 presents the discharge parameter curve typical for this case. One might allocate some characteristic features:
. sharp characteristic rise in the first 12 hours, from 16:00 until 04:00;
. the preservation of this high level for 4 hours;
. sharp glow drop in 20 hours after the death;
. preservation of constant glow level until the end of the experiment with gradually decreasing oscillations close in amplitude to limits of error.

I must admit that after obtaining these data at the end of this experiment I was rather disappointed. To work for four days with double holiday payment and to receive a straight line! It seemed to be a waste of time and money! However, this result had a redeeming quality: at the very start of our work we received solid proof of the objectivity of obtained data and their independence from any external conditions. Really, if the obtained parameters rise in the previous experiment had been caused by any instrumental error, fluctuation of radio wave propagation at night, atmospheric processes etc.; they would have been observed every night, or, anyway, nearly every night. But in the given case 20 hours after the death we received the direct line in greatly changed meteorological conditions. So this experiment increased our assurance of the necessity of further experiments. But how good that it was not the first!

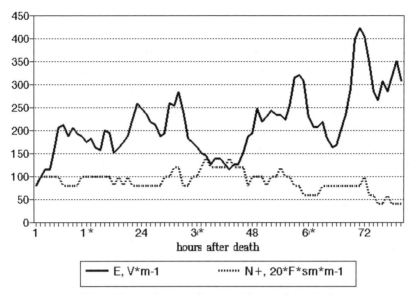

Fig. 2.12. Time dependence of atmospheric electrical parameters during experiment N2. E - amplitude of electrical field at surface level; N - electrical conductivity of air.

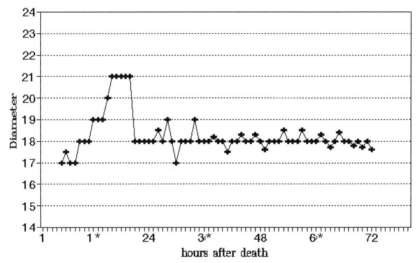

Fig. 2.13. Time dependence of Kirlian glow diameter of a finger for experiement N2. Vertical axis represents the area of a picture; horizontal axis represents time in hours after death. Fore finger.

# Experiment N 3

The data were taken from 19:00 March 12 (6 hours after the death) until 12:00 March 15. Death occurred at approximately 13:00 March 12. Man, 49 years of age, committed suicide by hanging himself in his own apartment.

Atmospheric conditions: March 12—increased pressure area, March 13—anticyclone centered above the Northern Atlantic, March 14—cyclone back with its center above the Barents sea, March 15—cyclone. Atmospheric pressure 757/761/765 mm.Hg. Ozone content 330/297/344 D.U., summarized radiation 5.31/5.42/2.68 MJ/m2, humidity 50/94/96%. Electric field and conductivity change curves are presented in Fig. 2.14.

A discharge characteristic curve is presented in Fig. 2.15. In this curve one can see the following features:
- a sharp rise of the characteristic during the first hours after the beginning of the experiment;
- powerful peak during overnight hours with a subsequent deep drop presented by a series of sequential points, with characteristic small maxima at the fall of the peak;
- subsequent rise with maxima during the second night;
- deep drop 47 hours after the death;
- subsequent practically continuous rise during 10 hours until the end of the process.

So in this experiment we see the "activity" of the curve greatly exceeding not only the second but also the first case. The comparison of results will be given in the following chapter in greater details.

# Experiment N 4

The data were taken from 18:00 (1 hour after the death) March 19 until 12:00 March 22. Death occurred at 17:00 March 19 as a result of closed-scull brain injury after a collision with a train. Broken shoulder and thigh. A man, approximately 30 years old.

Atmospheric conditions: March 19-20—cyclone with its center above the Northern Atlantic, March 21-22—cyclone forward part, from 14:00—warm cyclone sector with the center above Barents sea. Atmospheric pressure 740/742/754 mm.Hg., ozone content 387/448/427 D.E., summarized radiation 3.68/6.74/5.39 MJ/m2, humidity 71/90/96% Electrical field and conductivity curves are presented in Fig.2.16. Fig.2.17 presents a chart of one

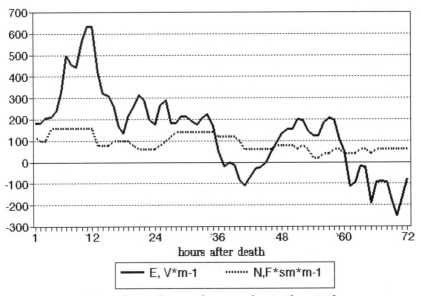

*Fig. 2.14. Time dependence of atmospheric electrical parameters during experiment N3. E - amplitude of electrical field at surface level; N - electrical conductivity of air.*

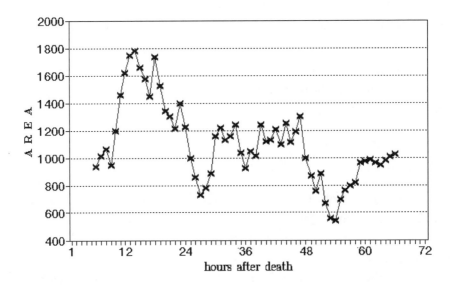

*Fig. 2.15. Time dependence of Kirlian glow area of a finger for experiment N3. Vertical axis represents the area of an image; horizontal axis represents time in hours after death. Fore finger.*

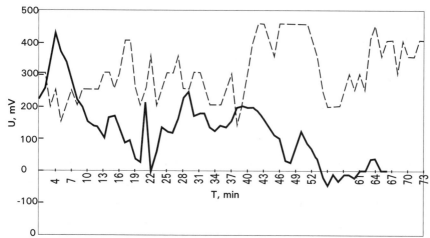

Fig. 2.16. Time dependence of atmospheric electrical parameters during experiment N4. E - amplitude of electrical field at surface level; N - conductivity of air.

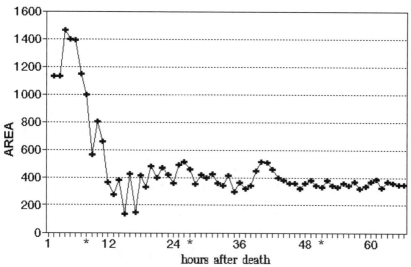

Fig. 2.17. Time dependence of Kirlian glow area of a finger for experiment N4. The vertical axis represents the area of an image; the horizontal axis is time in hours after death. Fore finger.

discharge parameter change. Note that in this experiment the work was begun an hour after the death while before we were able to begin during 4-6 hours period. In this chart the following features are seen:

- a sharp rise three hours after the death and then no less sharp drop during 6 hours; this drop corresponds to the over-night hours.

. subsequent condition from 14 to 40-44 hours after the death can be characterized as oscillatory; a peak amplitude in this period is not very high, therefore a small peak during the second night seems not to be important;

. stationary condition after 44 hours until the end of process .

The parameter behavior in this experiment is somewhat different from the cases considered above. The activity during overnight hours is not present here, but the stationary condition also comes, about two days after the death. It is interesting to mark a sharp burst immediately after the death and star-like spots of the type I have never seen before, corresponding to this burst on the photos. These spots practically disappear 5 hours after death. It is possible that we could have found these spots in other cases as well, had we been able to start our experiments sooner after death.

## Experiment N 5

Data were taken from 21:00 March 26 (3 hours after death) until 12:00 March 29. Death occurred at 18:00 March 26 as a result of scull-brain injury due to a car accident. A man, approximately 30 years old, his scull broken, brain is practically absent.

Atmospheric conditions: low gradient field of increased pressure. Atmospheric pressure 760/770/775 mm.Hg., ozone content 356/387/425 D.U., summarized radiation 6.79/4.18/12.89 MJ/m2, humidity 95/74/100%. As seen from Fig.2.18, electric field in the days of experiments had a strong oscillation, the number of charged particles strongly varied as well.

In the given case the above-noted features are repeated (Fig. 2.19):

. on the first and the second night maxima observed, though on the first night the rise begins after the midnight and proceeds 6 hours, replaced then by a larger maximum;

. on the second night the maximum is not strongly pronounced on the background of previous and subsequent oscillations;

. Sharp drop in the vicinity of the first day fall and after 38 hours;

. Further quasi stationary conditions until the end of the work.

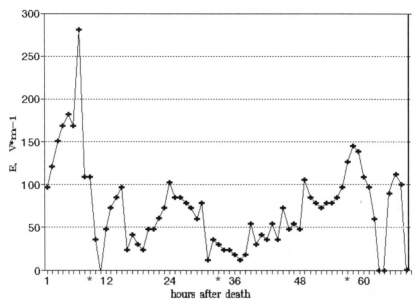

Fig. 2.18. Time dependence of atmospheric electrical parameters during experiment N5. E - amplitude of electrical field at surface level; N - conductivity of air.

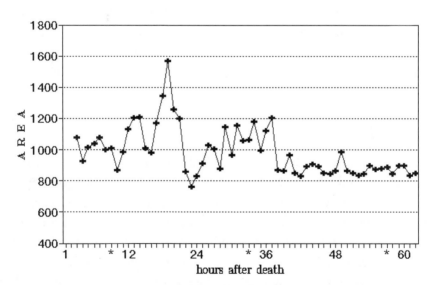

Fig. 2.19. Time dependence of Kirlian glow area of a finger for experiment N5. The vertical axis represents the area of an image; the horizontal axis is time in hours after death. Fore finger.

# Experiment N 6

Data were taken from 17:00 April 2 (2 hours after the death) until 09:00 April 5. Death occurred at 15:00 April 2. Diagnosis: hypertension, brain edema. A woman, 70 years old.

Atmospheric conditions: low gradient field of increased pressure. Atmospheric pressure 762/770/772 mm. Hg., ozone content 337/322/367 D.U., summarized radiation 10.25/15.70/6.47 MJ/m2, humidity 61/91/98%. As is clear from the curves Fig.2.20, alongside with strong fluctuations of summarized sun radiation all days of the experiment strong oscillations of electrical parameters in atmosphere were observed.

A discharge parameter curve (Fig. 2.21) shows the only explicitly expressed peak: between 13 and 20 hours; single peaks during the 26th and the 31st hour is insufficiently pronounced, as it is represented by one point. So it is not possible to speak of any special features here. One can note that in 48 hours region the curve activity substantially decreases. The total scope of oscillations is relatively weak: not to take into account the burst during the 31st hour, it takes about 400 units. For comparison one should note that in experiment N1 the range of this parameter change was 1100 units, in experiment N3—1300 units. So it is apparent that there exists no correlation between discharge and atmospheric parameters that is, electromagnetic processes in atmosphere do not influence the gas discharge characteristic.

# Experiment N 7

Data were taken from 21:00 April 16 (only 1 hour after the death) until 10:00 April 19. Death took place at 20:00 April 16. Death circumstances are tragically sad. A young girl, 19 years old, the day after her birthday went to a party with her friends. During the meal she had an asthma attack and took a medicine which caused vomiting. She tried to suppress vomiting which caused windpipe blocking. Someone applied assisted respiration to the girl in a faint which caused dense blocking of the windpipe. The doctor who came 20 minutes later was not able to return her to life despite his attempts. The autopsy showed that the bronchial tubes were densely blocked by vomiting masses.

Atmospheric conditions: low gradient field of increased pressure. Atmospheric pressure 753/756/744, mm.Hg. ozone content 330/343/380 D.U., summarized radiation 18.55/17.19/5.03 MJ/m2, humidity 47/55/96%

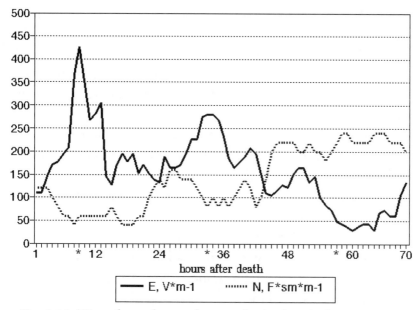

Fig. 2.20. *Time dependence of atmospheric electrical parameters during experiment N6. E - amplitude of electrical field at surface level; N - electrical conductivity of air.*

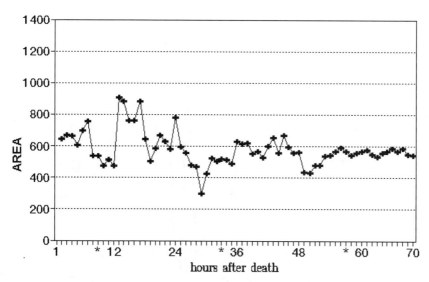

Fig. 2.21. *Time dependence of Kirlian glow area of a finger for experiment N6. The vertical axis represents the area of an image; the horizontal axis is time in hours after death. Fore finger.*

Electrical atmosphere parameters had large fluctuations especially in the last two days of experiment (Fig. 2.22).

Fig. 2.23, 2.24 present charts of glow area changes for two fingers. We presented two charts here in order to demonstrate their correlation once more and to reveal the most important curve node points. One can see the following features of these curves:

- small growth from the moment of measurement beginning (19:00) until 01:00, after that a relatively smooth drop sometimes followed by oscillations;
- powerful peak of practically identical shape for both curves from 13 until 22 hours after the death;
- two sharp drops: in 37 hours and in 44 hour;
- oscillatory nature of the process during all the period with gradual decrease but without achieving a stationary level, characteristic of most the cases considered earlier;
- as before, the correlation between the experimental curves and the meteorological data was not noted.

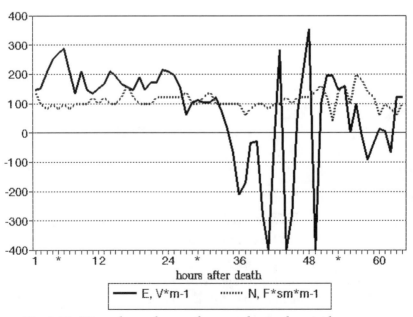

Fig. 2.22. Time dependence of atmospheric electrical parameters during experiment N7. E - amplitude of electrical field at surface level; N - electrical conductivity of air.

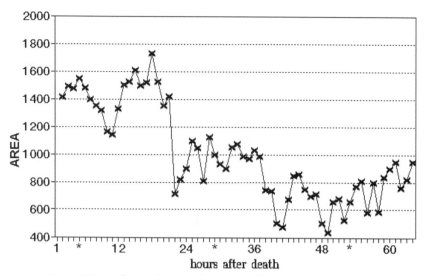

Fig. 2.23. *Time dependence of Kirlian glow area of a finger for experiment N7. The vertical axis represents the area of a picture; the horizontal axis is time in hours after death. Middle finger.*

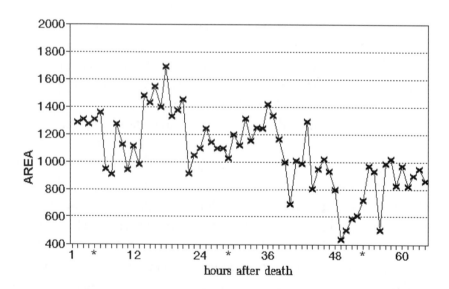

Fig. 2.24. *Time dependence of Kirlian glow area of a finger for experiment N7. The vertical axis represents the area of a picture; the horizontal axis is time in hours after death. Ring finger.*

# Experiment N 8

Data were taken from 10:00 May 1 (3 hours after the death) until 10:00 May 4. Death occurred at 07:00 May 1 as a result of a stroke. A man, 45-50, homeless, severely exhausted.

Atmospheric conditions: low gradient field of increased pressure. Atmospheric pressure 767/769/771 mm.Hg., ozone content 380/330/366 D.U., summarized radiation 15.58/22.68/22.68 MJ/m2, humidity 30/42/64%. From Fig.2.25 it is seen that strong oscillation of electrical atmosphere parameters began on the 2-3d day of the experiment.

As can be seen from the discharge curve (Fig. 2.26), oscillations of insignificant amplitude are seen approximately 45 hours after the death. No distinct features on the curve are observed.

# Experiment N 9

Data were taken from 03:00 May 29 (3 hours after the death) until 13:00 May 31. Death occurred at midnight May 29. A strong heart attack. An old man, 70.

Atmospheric conditions: low gradient field of lowered pressure. Atmospheric pressure 755/760/760 mm.Hg., ozone content 346/360/383 D.U., summarized radiation 26.21/20.51/27.01 MJ/m2, humidity 30/60/80%. On those days especially strong oscillations of electrical atmosphere parameters were not noted.

The discharge parameter curve (Fig. 2.27) demonstrates two small peaks in the first 16 hours after the death, therefore the oscillations of the amplitude can be compared with amplitude fluctuations. As before, in the case described the correlation with atmospheric parameters (Fig. 2.28) is not observed.

Concluding this chapter to demonstrate the range of experimental errors we present the time curve of benchmark object glow curve. As a benchmark object we used a glass test tube with physiological solution. Discharge photos of this object were produced during each test and it served for control of equipment and processing operation. As is clear from Fig. 2.29, the benchmark object curve, presented in the same coordinate system as the experimental data, has a small oscillation range although in some experiments the bursts of approximately two times greater amplitude were observed. In such cases the amplitude of the appropriate experimental point was correlated too.

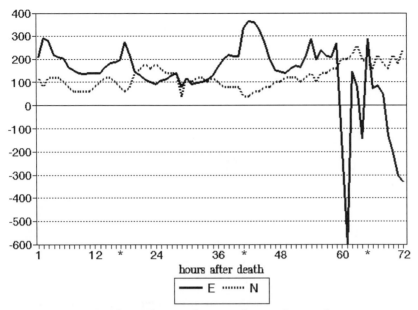

Fig. 2.25. Time dependence of atmospheric electrical parameters during experiment N8. E - amplitude of electrical field at surface level; N - electrical conductivity of air.

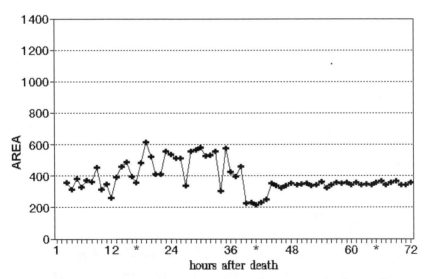

Fig. 2.26. Time dependence of Kirlian glow area of a finger for experiment N8. The vertical axis represents the area of an image; the horizontal axis is time in hours after death. Fore finger.

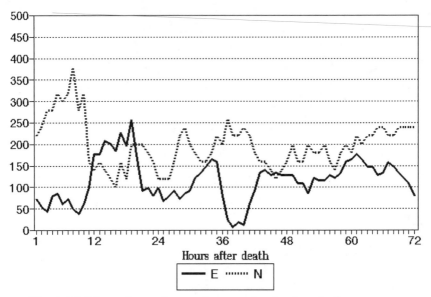

Fig. 2.27. *Time dependence of atmospheric electrical parameters during experiment N9. E - amplitude of electrical field at surface level; N - electrical conductivity of air.*

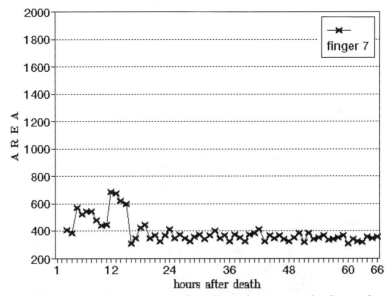

Fig. 2.28. *Time dependence of Kirlian glow area of a finger for experiment N9. The vertical axis represents the area of an image; the horizontal axis is time in hours after death. Fore finger.*

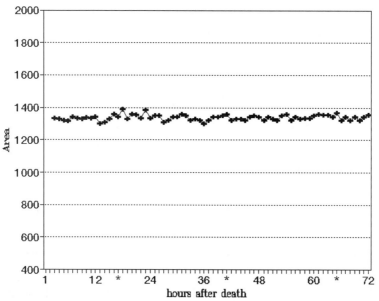

*Fig. 2.29. Time dependence of Kirlian glow area of a benchmark object during experiment N8. The vertical axis represents the area of an image; the horizontal axis is time in hours after death. Fore finger.*

# Discussion of experimental data

*No, there could be no error here:*
*the real sense of my life*
*exactly in what will be with me*
*after death.*
                    Robert Merl, "Madrapur"

## Basic classification

To evaluate the meaning of the submitted data it is necessary first of all to make the classification, that is to divide it into groups. The most natural classification principle seems to be in accordance with the amplitude of curve oscillations. This permits us to divide the data into three groups:

   I. Curves with relatively weak oscillation amplitude (area curve oscillations range not more than 600 units); to this group one might attribute the results of experiments N 2,6,8,9.

II. Curves with relatively weak oscillation amplitude but with one pronounced peak; experiments N 4,5.

III. Large amplitude curves (area curve oscillation range is more than 600 units) with oscillations of long-duration; experiments N 1,3,7.

Each of these groups is characterized by a specific death cause:

group I: "calm, natural" death caused by the conditions of body tissues.

group II: "violent" death as a result of a traffic accident with scull—brain injury.

group III: "unexpected" death as a result of some tragic circumstances which in more favorable conditions could have been avoided.

I want to stress that the above division is rather tentative and in no way is final. It's quite possible that later the principle of classification will substantially change. For example case N 1 as seen from the curve belongs to group III though the death cause might with full right be identified as natural. Successes of medicine in this century put off the death threshold for earlier incurable cases. Therefore, the given death might scarcely be classified as natural. Case 5 in accordance with the curve character might be attributed to group III, however it is more interesting to group it with case 4. Besides, such division is confirmed by discharge photos grouping to be discussed below. At the given stage there is too little data for final classification, therefore allocated groups should be considered as preliminary, however even such preliminary analysis permits sometimes to see the data in a new light and thus to lay the base for further experiments.

Let us note the main features of curves common to each group.

**group I.** On the curve one might allocate two segments: oscillations exceeding benchmark level and comparable with benchmark; duration of the first segment is from 16 to 55 hours, it is scarcely expedient to allocate any features to these sites.

**group II.** Explicitly pronounced peak in one case corresponds to the first 8 hours after death, in the other case—the end of the first day; oscillations come to benchmarck level approximately two days after the death.

**group III.** In this group the most explicitly represented features common for all three cases are as follows:

- high amplitude and duration of oscillations as compared with the previous groups;

- reduction of amplitude from the beginning to the end of experiment—peaks at night from 21:00, of various rate and duration;
- local glow drop at the end of the first day and a sharp drop at the end of the second day.

Allocated groups are distinguished also by common glow nature which is seen from finger glow prints received after computer processing (Fig. 2.30).

At the start of experiment     At the end of experiment

*Fig. 2.30. Processed images of Kirlian glow.*

**group I** The crown consists of separate branch-like streamers arranged at a distance from each other; in accordance with chapter-2 classification it is N-type picture, in some cases D-type; glow nature practically does not vary to the end of experiment if a small reduction of intensity is not taken into consideration.

**group II**. A more dense and uniform glow than in the previous case, it might be attributed rather to type-L; by the end of the experiment the crown density drops, the type being transformed to N.

**group III**. Continuous uniform glow crown practically without breakage; the example referred to by Mandel as a "terrible" radiation and in our classification related to V-type; by the end of the experiment the glow rate sharply drops and it transforms to L-type.

So in all cases the glow type corresponds to a "bad" condition of energy, at the same time being different between groups. As was noted in chapter 4, glows of type N and D are inherent to people with suppressed energy, unable to mobilize protective forces to struggle with illnesses and infections. This type is frequently seen in a senile person. Type N is frequently seen in "practically healthy" people, having a lot of diseases. Type V, as was noted earlier, was observed quite seldom in cases of pathological processes, although we can't attribute this type for sure: with certain difficulty this glow can be referred to as R-type.

Let us note one more main feature of the obtained data. While planning the experiments we hoped to determine the cause of death by the photos, that is the main disease, in the case of a "natural" death at least.

Really, the glow features of types K,R,L of leaving persons show their organism diseases, so one could expect that these features would remain some time after the death. But it was not so in cases 6,8,9, where data was taken 2-3 hours after the death. Future experiments, which will take place in departments of intensive care with the fixation of the moment of transition from this world to the other, will show whether this feature characterizes only this set of experiments or reflects some basic feature of a human organism.

We see that in accordance with the glow type the objects under study divide in logical groups coinciding with previous classification. So far we have presented all the experimental facts, which can be appreciated in different ways by different readers.

We tried to submit the material with all details, so that the reader can on the one hand see all possible errors missed by the author, and on the other hand have an opportunity of independently reproducing the experiments under discussion.

Only further research in this direction can reveal the true importance of the results obtained and determine the way of their interpretation.

# Part III.

# The Concept of Morphogenetic Synergization of Biological Objects

*"I could a tale unfold, whose lightest word*
*Would harrow up thy soul"*
William Shakespeare, *"Hamlet"*

*Co-authored with*
*Dr. Alexander Kouznetsov*

# Introduction

This American edition appears more than two years after the first experimental results were published. During this time the collected data was substantially extended—both through our own study and through the research of other laboratories in Russia. The general results and their classification were fully confirmed, though, as expected, this first iteration seems to be rough in a way.

Today the application of the developed technique is under a very intensive study in the field of criminology. In some cases the knowledge of the psycho-emotional state of a person at the moment of death could help determine whether or not it was a murder.

The practical significance of the results is already beyond doubts. At the same time, it is still increasingly challenging to comprehend and explain the inner clockwork mechanisms of this phenomenon. From the very beginning we tried to look for an explanation only in the science. We do not deny mystical and religious theories, but we do consider the power of the modern science far from being exhausted. The task demanded a profound study of many branches of science, including some new directions, and communication with many scientists and experts in their fields.

Still, the author found a most fruitful source of everyday theoretical and practical inspiration in his cooperation with an old friend, a cybernetics specialist, Dr. A.L.Kouznetsov. Dr. Kouznetsov's attitude gradually evolved from skepticism to attentive consideration. Then, in a sudden insight, Dr. Kouznetsov grasped the complexity and beauty of the entire issue and was at once charmed by it. Many hours of jogging in St. Petersburg parks, climbing in the mountains of Caucasus and Pamir, hiking in Bavaria and Chamonix gave us with enough time to discuss, sketch out and develop the concept for this book.

One feature of the chosen approach is that a wide class of non-traditional phenomena could be explained without the development of a new apparatus. The concept is based on the generalization of the well-known and accepted perceptions of modern science. In accordance with this theory, anomalous phenomena are but a boundary manifestations of known laws. At the same time, the concept presents a view of the world as a boundless hierarchical network of entities with an unlimited complexity of interactions and influences. This network is self-developing; it grows increasingly sophisticated throughout multi-level feedback:

- Universal Information Field, generated by billions of human minds and existing through them;
- Biological Field, being understood as a system integrity of physical fields and informational influences;
- unity of the material and the spiritual, the unity of science, religion and spirituality.

It is very encouraging to be able to trace the roots of nearly all new ideas to the depths of ancient philosophical systems of the East and the West. Interpreted in a modern scientific way, they mark a monumental chain of spiritual self-exploration of mankind, founded by the wisemen of India, China, Greece and for a short (on the scale of history) period abandoned for the cold hypocrisy of materialism. As the specter of Communism ceases to haunt the world, the world begins to awaken from the lethargy of the materialistic way of thinking. The human mind returns to the freedom of spirit enriched with new approaches proven through the technical progress of civilization. The unification of spirit and technology could help mankind make a new step - or, maybe, the first step out of the dead-end we are in now.

This section of the book has the following structure. **Chapter 1** contains a review of the current situation and of the topic in general. After a study of some interesting facts and a discussion on the connections between Cosmos and Life, we come to the definition of the *biological field* and understand that it is based upon many primary perceptions, first and foremost the *information* and the *energy*. **Chapter 2** deals with the following thought: What is the role of energy and information in maintaining the life of biological objects? What is information from the point of view of *cybernetics, information theory, system approaches*? Answers to these questions inevitably lead us to the introduction of the concepts of *synergetics*—a new synthetic science of the 20th century. The basic principles of synergetics and its applications in our everyday life are discussed in **Chapter 3**. **Chapter 4** focuses on the physical fields of biological objects within the wide range of the wave band. Here we introduce the notion of *spin-torsion fields*—one of the latest discoveries of modern theoretical physics. The authors of this model perceive the fields as the most important carrier of information between biological objects due to their unusual properties. However difficult it is to evaluate the real significance of this concept just now, it seems interesting enough to keep an eye on its development.

These four chapters are but a survey guiding the readers toward **Chapter 5**, which leads the main line of the study. Here the principal concept of the *resonance synchronization* of biological objects is introduced. The explanations of the concept are based both on the genetic structure of organisms and on general synergetics principles.

The concept of the resonance synchronization of the field structures of separate organs enables us to speak about the entire 3-dimensional interferential structure of the organism itself. This structure is holographic by nature and in **Chapter 6** we discusses several ancient and modern analogues of this concept.

The perception of the biological field, introduced in this manner, can be very well correlated with energy and information centers of the body—*Chakras*. This correlation naturally follows the consideration of the process of *embryogenesis*: from an initial spherically-symmetrical population of cells to a complicated material-field structure. In **Chapter 7** the hypothesis of the *acupuncture system* of points and channels as projections of the field structure on the surface of the body is discussed.

Several important consequences follow this hypothesis:

- an organism could have not only one, but many different field structures and, correspondingly, many skin projections;
- any small part of the field structure bears all the properties of the whole;
- the field structure is spread beyond the body surface and, in principle, fill the whole Universe;
- the source-organism's field structure could be reproduced in any domain of the Universe;

**Chapter 8** deals with the introduction and definition of *Energy/Information Structure* of biological object. The content of this term is discussed and the concept of the hierarchical structure of organisms is examined. The perceptions, introduced for a single organism in **Chapter 9**, are generalized for a group of organisms. The concept of *structural synchronization* within a group is introduced. This enables us to derive several consequences of significant methodological importance. **Chapter 10** is dedicated to the examination of different levels of synchronization. Finally, in **Chapter 11**, an attempt is made to apply all the developed principles to interpret the results of the study of processes after Death.

The main goal of this book is to make ideas simple to grasp, sacrificing the formality of reasoning. This trade-off is very familiar to many authors of popular-science books.

The discussions and disputes with our colleagues after first publications and conferences helped structure many questions and identify new problems. There is much work to do, and that by itself is very encouraging: it shows that this newly open field can be a fertile one. Let us crop the harvest together!

#  The Basics

*There are more things in heaven and earth, Horatio,*
*Than are dreamt of in your philosophy.*
　　　　　*Shakespeare. Hamlet. 1.5.*

**Does our Consciousness linger after our Death? What is Consciousness from the Physical point of view? What is the role of biological objects in the Universe? What is The Concept of Biological Fields?**

Before answering the first of these questions we should understand the nature of consciousness, and its role in the physical world. This section introduces the concept of the consciousness, developed on the basis of modern physical perceptions, and helps to understand several important peculiarities of Man's developing and behavior.

❖ ❖ ❖

In 1945 one of the founders of quantum mechanics, Ervine Shröedinger, published a book titled "What is Life?", where he studied the living object from the point of view of thermodynamics (a science dealing with the general relationship between heat and other forms of energy). The main ideas were as follows.

How does an organism develop? We commonly speak of the number of calories, accepted from a food, air, sun; i.e. with respect to energy. Does this mean that we constantly add new energy to the pool already existing in the organism? Certainly not, since at the same time we spend some, so our organism as a whole is in a state of balance with the surrounding environment, the state of homeostasis.

Let us assume that a system could have many different states with different energy and some of the states could have the same energy $E$. Accordingly, some of the values of $E$ are more probable to be found in a system than the other, since they are more frequent. Let us denote the probability of the system to have the energy $E$ as $P(E)$. The higher $P(E)$ is, the bigger the corresponding number of states, i.e. it is more difficult to predict the concrete state of the system.

In practice it is more convenient to deal not with P(E), but rather with $ln$P(E) since this function varies much less with E. The value of $ln$P(E) is already a numeric measure for the disorder in the system. In thermodynamics it is more common to deal with the function $k\ ln$P(E), where $k$ is a constant with the value measured in energy units (Boltzman constant). This function S is called entropy:

$$S = k\ ln\ P(E)$$

Some technical applications, thermodynamics most of all, are more convenient to discuss in terms of entropy rather than energy. In this sense, the balance of the energy could be defined as the balance of entropy:

$$dS = dS^{(food)} + dS^{(env)}$$

The change of entropy dS in the organism is equal to the sum of the entropy resulting from the consumption of food, air, light $dS^{(food)}$ and the entropy given out to the environment $dS^{(env)}$.

For an adult person in the state of homeostasis with the environment, dS = 0 (in other words, his state and his weight practically remain the same), or

$$dS(food) + dS(env) = 0$$

and

$$dS(food) = - dS(env)$$

In accordance to the Shröedinger's terminology, the organism "produces" a negative entropy. As assumed by Shröedinger, this negative entropy separates the living from the inanimate nature. A stone, accepting the energy of the sun, only becomes heated, i.e. increases its entropy, while the entropy of a living being can remain constant.

For a child the outflow of entropy exceeds its production—a child consumes more of "negative entropy". For an older organism the growth of entropy is not compensated by the outflow.

The entropy reaches its maximum level in the balance state of death.

It is possible to draw a simplified graph of entropic changes during the lifetime of an organism (Fig.3.1). In childhood, the outflow of entropy exceeds its influx. The adult organism keeps entropy around a constant level. At an older age entropy climbs to its maximum value. The lower line shows entropic exchange with the surrounding environment—or the production of *negative* entropy by the living organism. When comparing these two lines, one can see

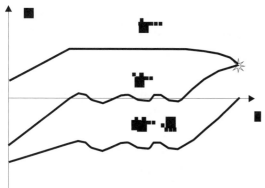

*Fig. 3.1. Simplified graph of entropic changes during the lifetime of an organism.*

that the less food a person consumes, the closer he comes to the balance state. (It is hard not to recall Paul Bregg and other proponents of fasting).

The work of Shröedinger marked the beginning of a new stage of natural science development: an integration of different disciplines, rather than their specialization. Modern science takes a similar position in studying the *Benar effect*, the *laser emission*, the *morphogenesis*, the *heart fibrillation*. It is proven that order can be born of chaos by such processes as phase transitions. Cooperative processes in plasma, the Northern Lights, periodical cloud structures, and sea waves are all manifestation of the same laws. From this point of view, the definition of life, given by Shröedinger, turned out to be limited. The outflow of entropy is the property of many self-organization processes in the still nature. One can even say that it is a precondition for the appearance of any sophisticated structure. Cosmic, geological, biological evolutionary processes of the "order-emerging-from-chaos" are the result of entropy export to the surrounding media. Life, and conscious life in particular, is the unique phenomenon of the universe, which cannot be described by thermodynamic features alone. Later we will show that modern science is able to define all its peculiarities more precisely. Let us start with the discussion of the role and the place of the human being in the universe.

As long ago as we know, people have been trying to comprehend the role of the mind in the universe. Ranging from primitive superstitions to profound

*Fig. 3.2. Some ancient perceptions of the world*

philosophical abstractions, some of these attempts now appear amusing (Fig.3.2). But who can say that the next generation will not regard the Big Bang as an irresistibly hilarious idea, and many of the ancient concepts as sound and unquestionable. At any rate, we have always felt ourselves closely connected to the cosmos. It is quite natural that we, as an observer of the outer world, have always put ourselves right in the center of the universe, whether physically or psychologically.

Possible subjective reasons for this can be found in an interesting observation made by Suchonos [Suchonos, 1981]. He proposed a universal variation scale. All the objects of the universe can be distributed in accordance with their characteristic dimension "L". The starting point is defined by the Planck's constant:

$$n = 10^{43} \text{ Hz,} - t = 10^{-43} \text{ s,} - L = 10^{-33} \text{ cm.}$$

This is a barrier, impenetrable to modern theoretical physics. The upper boundary is set by the size of the expanding *metagalaxy*. (In accordance with modern cosmological perceptions, this process started 15-20 billion years ago, i.e. $10^{17}$ seconds. Between then and now, an electromagnetic wave would run

| LIFE | | | | | | | | | | | |
|---|---|---|---|---|---|---|---|---|---|---|---|
| Pre-cellular & single-cell | | | Multi-cell | | | Biogeonesis | | | | | |
| Electron | | Atom | | Human | | Star | | Galaxy | | | |
| $10^{-33}$ | $10^{-28}$ | $10^{-23}$ | $10^{-18}$ | $10^{-13}$ | $10^{-8}$ | $10^{-3}$ | $10^{2}$ | $10^{7}$ | $10^{12}$ | $10^{17}$ | $10^{22}$ | $10^{27}$ | L, cm |

*Fig.3.3. A scale for ranging the objects of the Universe in accordance with their characteristic dimensions "L".*

the distance of $10^{28}$ cm.) An example of this systematization is shown in Fig.3.3.

As one can see from the figure, the atoms, human beings, stars and galaxies differ from each other in size by a factor of $10^{10}$. This means that the hierarchy of universe's entities has a certain module of regularity. It is interesting to note, that the zone of life is located just in the middle of this scale.

Suchonos claims also that the galaxy with its characteristic size $L=10^{22}$ develops from a nucleus sized $10^{17}$, while an adult man ($L=10^{2}$) develops from a cell sized $10^{-3}$. In both cases the difference is $10^{5}$ times, i.e. the development of a man and a galaxy follow the same dimensional ratio. Maybe the intuitive recognition of this, as well as other similar facts, drove ancient people to connect the structure of the universe with that of man. The keystone of this connection is the perception of a field in different forms.

In the beginning of this century, modern science revived these representations in the form of the *biological field*. This concept was independently put forth by Alexander Gurwitsch, 1922; Hans Spemann, 1938; Paul Weiss, 1939.

In accordance with the paradigm of the contemporary science, the field was declared to be electromagnetic (EM). Detailed description of these ideas can be found in later works [Kazhinskii, 1963; H.S.Burr, 1972]. However, more elaborate considerations forced the scientific world to abandon this idea. Though extremely important for the life processes in organism, *EM Waves* (EMW) cannot be responsible for the whole spectrum of phenomena we observe in this world. Most importantly, they cannot be responsible for morphogenesis. The main objections against EM theory of the bio-field are as follows:

. EMW can be too easily modulated, distorted and screened; many natural phenomena (from thunderstorm to geomagnetism) could serve as their source. Hence, any information carried by EMW is inevitably distorted;

. Transmission (propagation) of EMW over long distances is connected with a considerable energy consumption. Simple calculations show that EM field of bio-objects could not expand longer than for several meters, a fact confirmed by modern scientific measurements.

Hence, there is no reason to establish the existence of any universal field in this waveband.

Significant progress has been achieved by the Cambridge biologist Rupert Sheldrake. Working in the field of theoretical evolutionary biology, Sheldrake published two books (1981, 1988) in which he introduced the concept of "formative causation", based on the hypothesis of *morphogenetic fields*. The Greek word *"morfe"* means "a form", hence "morphogenetic" is "producing forms". Sheldrake's notion is very similar to Aristotle's idea that universe consists of both *matter* and *form*. In Aristotle's understanding, matter is the potential energy. There is no "existence" in matter itself; there is the "potentiality to exist".

Matter is structured by form, or *eidos*. The Greek word *"eidos"* first meant "a form" in the literal sense (for example, the shape of a stone or a dog); then it came to mean an organizing power (of the stone or the dog). Matter is indeterminate and unstructured, which is the source of all indeterminacy and unpredictability of the material world. Matter is organized only by the form.

Sheldrake introduced the idea of morphogenetic fields—applying it not only to living beings, but to all objects in the universe. This means that each living or non-living entity develops its particular form (as a crystal, or organ, or plant, or animal), because it is placed in a particular (structuring) morphogenetic field. This particular structuring is possible due to the *morphic resonance*, i.e. a resonance between similar elements. Sheldrake claims that the field contains an inherent memory.

To illustrate the difference between the mechanistic view and his own position, Sheldrake uses the analogy of a radio. The radio set is a mechanistic (not mechanical, but electronic) system, which works properly only when it is in operating condition. But the proper operating condition itself is insufficient, since the radio receiver also must be tuned to its environment (specific frequencies). The materialistic view demands everything to be explained in terms of the mechanism of the radio set only. For instance, if you play this radio while visiting a primitive tribe in Africa, the audience may very well think that the voices are coming directly from the radio set itself. What is more, they would be able to prove it: the moment the set is broken, the voices would stop; as soon as the set is repaired, the voices would come back again. It would be all too easy for them to conclude that the voices could be explained in terms of the mechanism.

In the mechanistic model of the Universe it is quite true that when the mechanism goes wrong (when, for instance, the brain fails), it ceases to operate (the mind stops acting). Still, the mind cannot be reduced to the brain alone. Proper operation of the brain is a condition that is necessary but not sufficient. In case of the radio, the voices cannot be explained through the knowledge of what happens inside the radio. Moreover, the signals carrying the voices come from outside of the radio receiver and have an entirely different nature then the radio set itself.

Similarly, in the process of evolution, one can distinguish the material aspect of matter, which embodies it in accordance with the mechanistic laws (like the radio set itself), and also formative aspects, the effect of which is to organize the matter. Each particular kind of the matter "tunes in" to its own particular field. As an organism starts to develop, it begins to resonate to a certain field, and the more the organism follows that particular path, the more it becomes habituated and easy to develop (within that field) toward its final form.

Sheldrake gives a wide range of biological examples supporting his ideas. Through his books, translated into a number of languages, his newspaper articles, TV-shows etc., these ideas became widely known all over the world. Thus, morphogenetic fields are seen to be an important component in the development of a new understanding of evolution. Sheldrake only postulated the existence of these fields, but suggested no explanations for their origin and nature. In this work we are not concerned with the biological justification of morphogenetic fields' necessity, since it has already been done by Sheldrake brilliantly. We concentrate on developing the physical concepts of these fields.

## Summary.

1. The concept of the biological field was introduced in the beginning of this century as an explanation of peculiarities of the development and functioning of biological objects. The concept, now widely used in biology, still requires a strict physical interpretation.

2. Attempts to connect this field to the *electromagnetic waveband* alone have been abandoned after a close consideration. The properties of EM field exclude it from being the only candidate for the biological field carrier.

3. Considerable progress has been achieved by R. Sheldrake, who introduced the idea of the *morphogenetic field*. Basing his conclusions on the study of many examples, he demonstrated the insufficiency of the modern science paradigm, and shown it to lack the form-building element. Still, R. Sheldrake proposed no physical mechanism behind this phenomenon.

# 2 What is information?

*"Polonius: What do you read, my lord?"*
*"Hamlet: Words, words, words."*
  *William Shakespeare, "Hamlet"*

Many centuries have passed since the question was posed for the first time, and still it remains a challenge for scientists: what does a person inherit, and what is brought to his personality later? The discovery of genetic mechanisms seemed for a time to converge toward a solution, but once again the reality turned out to be more complicated than could be imagined.

Several years ago a child was found in Brazil, whose heartless mother left him with the yard dogs after his father abandoned her. At the age of three, the child could only crawl on his fours (like a dog) and lap up from a saucer (like a dog). There was nothing apparently human in him.

Many true "Mowgli[1]" stories like this prove that it is not possible to bring those outcasts back to human behavior. That shows that besides genetic information an organism receives an additional information of some kind. Does anybody know what kind? And what is *information* itself? Let us concentrate on this definition. Traditionally, the concept of information is very closely tied with the already mentioned concept of entropy, the term initially introduced by R. Clausiuss to describe the performance of a heat engine. Later this notion played a very important role in thermodynamics, helping to define the laws of macroscopic system behavior.

Initially introduced for a special class of closed thermodynamic systems, later in this century, the concept was extended to measure disorganization in any kind of a system. This measure ranges from chaos, or total indetermination to absolute order (S=0).

The connection between entropy and information in implicit form was stated by L. Scillard in 1929. He noted that entropy lost by gas due to the separation of particles with high and low energy is equal to the information transmitted to the observer. The theory of information has been started by K. Shannon's works (1948). He understood *information* as a message, reducing the uncertainty (entropy) of the *message receiver*. Later N. Wiener linked the amount of information $J$ to the amount of thermodynamic negative entropy (S+$J$=const).

This enables us to regard information as one of the most fundamental characteristics of all natural phenomena. Juxtaposed with general categories like *matter* and *energy*, *information* gradually developed into a very deep and broad concept, growing still deeper and wider as we study it. Depending on the domain of knowledge of a particular science, information gets a context-specific definition:

- information denotes meaning received from the outside world in the process of adapting to it. (N. Winner);
- information is the negation of entropy (Brilluen);
- information is communication and connection, removing the uncertainty (Shannon);
- information is a measure of structural variety (Eshby);
- information is the reflected diversion (Ursul);
- information is a measure of the complexity of structures (Moll);

1   *Rudyard Kipling*

- information is a probability of choice (Yaglom) etc.

Depending on the contextual aspect, information is often divided into several categories [Abdeyev, 1994]:

- structural information—inherent in objects of both live and still nature, connected to the structure, composition and operation of these objects.
- operative information—dealing with a transmission of this information to other objects. In this case there should be a sender of the information, a receiver and a channel.

It is clear that both forms are interchangeable. The structural information of still nature proved to be a necessary precondition for the appearance of operational information and the functioning of live-nature systems. Both classes of information are very closely linked together by mutual transfers and interdependence.

As an example of a very sophisticated definition, we can quote academician Glushkov: "Information, in a most general sense, is a measure of heterogeneity of matter and energy distribution in time/space, a measure of changes accompanying all the processes in the world".

Let us note that, regardless of the variability of these definitions, they implicitly assume the existence of a receiver of information. Without an active "consumer", who is able to interpret the received message in a certain way, information does not manifest itself and remains a hidden property of the containing object. Everything just discussed enables us to introduce a generalized definition of information:

*Information is a fundamental property of matter, manifested in the process of goal-seeking activity.*

Let us logically expound on this definition, since it actually contains several statements. First, we connect the concept of information with matter. This means that information is not a separate entity, but rather a mandatory property of material objects and fields. Accordingly, the carriers of information can be both objects and fields.

Information cannot exist without a material carrier; it is not a material object but a philosophical category. Hence, it is possible to speak about informational fields, at the same time understanding very clearly that all fields should have certain carriers.

Let us stress that the same physical media can carry information and cause a direct influence—depending on the character of the receiving agent. For example, the same sunlight can be both informative (manifesting the beginning of the day) and effective (causing influence—burning the skin). A stone falling from the rock face could inform a climber about the potential danger (when flying by) and cause physical trauma (when hitting directly). But without the presence of the climber the same stone carries no information: nobody is receiving this information.

Second, information is an inherent material phenomenon, but it could exist concealed until the appearance of an active *agent* able to accept this information. To accept the information means that the agent will react in a way provisioned by the object goal-seeking procedure.

It is not necessary that the object manifesting goal-seeking behavior be a biological one; it can be any entity or phenomenon of the material world. The only important thing is that the goal is understood as an *attractor*.

The concept of the attractor is now very popular, due to the synergetics approach we will discuss later. The term 'attractor' came originally from the *dynamic systems theory*. Very often the behavior of dynamic systems is described in terms of some generalized coordinates which form the phase "portrait" of the system. Hence, the particular behavior of a system is represented by a point, moving along a certain trajectory in this space. Very often all the trajectories lead to the same point or an area, regardless of the starting point. It can be illustrated by a set of balls, rolling downhill into the same trough (Fig.3.4 a).

In dynamic systems theory, this "destination" is called *the solution*. The entire area, starting from which a system could come to the same destination, is called a *solution domain* (areas A and B on Fig. 3.4 b). Sometimes domains are separated by distinct borders, such as verges, saddles etc. In many practical cases the domains are not so clearly separated (for instance, the border could have a fractal character). In this case, one cannot predict the solution at which the system will arrive. Solutions act as if they "attract" the system, "competing" with each other. In case of biological systems, the main attractor is *survival*, i.e. the self-supporting process of life itself.

In this paradigm, even disease can be regarded as a goal-seeking process: a harmful agent is attracted to its own goal, acting as a parasite on the host organism. The latter tries to withstand this outer disturbance, being driven by its own attractor. Non-biological objects are also involved in some development processes, with their own global and local attractors.

So, a stone on the mountain slope has the position with the minimum potential energy as the attractor. The global attractor is the bottom of the

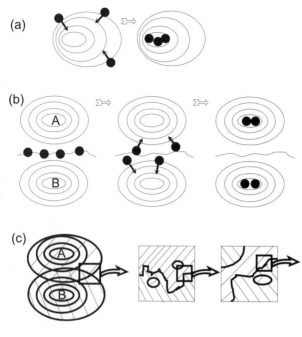

(a)

(b)

(c)

*Fig. 3.4. Dynamic Systems Theory representation.*

valley, while every hole on the slope is a local one. The stone is "purposely heading" for this position, but the character of this movement is passive.

The science disciplines of 60's (dynamic systems theory, optimization theory and other branches of cybernetics) normally concentrate on the study of system's behavior on its way to an attractor. Later came the understanding that attractors (and other singularity points) are **not** annoying bits of nuisance, blurring the crystal-clear mathematical picture of reality, but reality itself. The theory of catastrophes seemed to be a prophet, manifesting the appearance of a new messiah, a new meta-science paradigm: *synergetics*.

## Summary.

1. One of the most fundamental concept of the physical world, along with energy, mass and time, is the concept of information. The concept was introduced in the beginning of this century, but up to this time the different sciences have explored different aspects of information, depending on the application.

2. A new definition of information is introduced. The definition is explained and applied in terms of the perception of synergy.

# 3 Synergetic Universe

*"Time shall unfold what plaited cunning hides"*
William Shakespeare, *"King Lear"*

## 3.1. Brief History

What are the generally approved and accepted patterns specific to the classical science? This question is very important, since many stereotypes of a classically-oriented mind ("linear thinking" stereotypes) still remain.

The science of modern time - *classical science* - had been nourishing a strictly determined way of thinking. The ideals of scientific knowledge have been simplicity, linearity, total exclusion of indetermination (chance). There has always been a drive to establish universal physical laws (in the form of one-to-one functional correspondence), which would explain all phenomena of the real world. Causality has been regarded as an undesired factor of a minor significance. Our world was seen as affected neither by small fluctuations on the micro-level, nor by weak influences on the macro-level. Imbalance and instability were an irritating obstacle to be overcome by enhanced mathematics. All processes in the world have been thought to be repeatable in time, reconstructible for any time interval. Development was understood as linear and straightforward, having no alternatives. The world was properly built on the basis of *cause-effect sequence*, and all cause-effect chains were linear. Moreover, due to the logical equivalence of causes and effects, any development could be well predicted. The past was determinable by the future and vice versa.

Now this strictly determined perception of the world seems an oversimplified theoretical model. It does not include many important values—in the first place, time and random events. In the first half of 20$^{th}$ century, perception of the universe changed dramatically. Accordingly changed was the scientific paradigm—Einstein's theory of relativity and quantum mechanics came into play. It was discovered that causality and uncertainty are principally inherent to nature. Ever since, statistical laws have no longer been seen as temporary substitutions, 'patches' for exact physical laws, expected to be discovered later. Moreover, there appeared an even more 'extremist' point of view: to regard *statistical laws* as more fundamental laws of nature than the ones of classical science.

The practical outcome of this change of the classic paradigm resulted in the appearance of a new applied and a very practical science *cybernetics*. Cybernetics, in its turn, paved the way for the appearance of the newest scientific discipline of the 20th century *synergetics*.

The next section will be dedicated to a brief description of its fundamental principles.

## 3.2. Synergetic concept

All classical sciences deal with processes in so called "closed" systems, i.e. the systems not interacting with the outer world. In accordance with the Second Law of Thermodynamics, these systems tend toward a state with maximum entropy, i.e. toward utmost chaos. In particular, it gave life to the hypotheses of the death of the universe from heat. For more than a century this was a damnation for philosophers and natural scientists. The solution to this paradox was introduced and developed by proponents of the school of thought of the Nobel Prize winner Ilya Prigogine.

In their works they show that the idea of closed systems is too rough an idealization of reality. Our world is the world of interaction and open systems. Furthermore, these systems are non-linear: they cannot be represented by a sum or a superposition of their parts, and their response is not always proportional to input. More importantly, they are developing systems.

Systems of this kind are substantially unstable (i.e. all their balance states are unstable). Respectively, small (inner or outer) fluctuations could cause the system not to return back to its previous state, but develop in a very complicated way. In particular, a new structure could appear. This new structure will remain relatively stable, until a new fluctuation brings on a new change.

The main achievement of synergetics is the study of the system's behavior at decisive points of its development—the points of *bifurcation*. At these points the system "chooses" a direction to one attractor from many possible alternatives, i.e. selects a certain way of development. Often the different ways of systems' evolution can be explained through bifurcations, caused by the change of parameters of the outer environment. Within a certain range of variations the system still moves to the same attractor, but when a certain threshold is passed, behavior of the system changes dramatically. Variation of outer constants changes the whole landscape of the phase plane, where the evolution line of the system lies. When the surroundings change considerably (it could be a physical environment, composition of reacting chemical elements or biological media), it is quite natural to expect the appearance of new structures and new bifurcational ways of evolution.

In many real cases the attractor itself can be anything but simple. On a phase plane it may be impossible to represent it by a simple figure such as a point or asymptotic curve—perhaps a circle, ellipse, spiral etc. There could be so called *strange attractors*—certain areas, bounding chaotic movements of solution points. Systems with strange attractors cannot be referred to as absolutely unstable, since the solutions belong to a restricted area. They are relatively stable, but unpredictable in a classical way.

Synergetics leads us to a remarkable conclusion: our world seems to be stable, but it is only a relative stability, or a *meta-stability*. Complicated systems bear a trend for de-structuring after a certain development phase is passed. This instability is a dialectic category. Stability grows from instability and vice versa.

One of the central ideas of synergetics is the concept of a range of *development possibilities* for a certain class of open, non-linear systems. To a certain extent it is a determination, but one of a special kind. This range of predetermined possibilities forms a space of evolution. The system forms its own unique trace in this space, through a random choice. That is why all real phenomena are a mixture of a prescribed destiny and statistic fluctuations. So, the difference between the classical and the modern approaches is that the latter considers the future and the past to be connected only in a probable way. The present is just a realization of a random process. The present is still determined by the future, but only partly, through the given chain of attractors, by random moves from one attractor to the next.

The future defines the present, but it is an open definition. The choice of possibilities depends on fluctuations, presenting odds at the moment of partial bifurcation. Additionally, the open systems themselves also develop in the course of evolution, and the spectrum of possible evolutionary structures changes accordingly.

Synergetics has developed a perception of the world as a complex of interacting and mutually reflecting structures of different levels, forms, sizes, duration etc. Beyond a certain level of complexity, there could not be two totally identical objects in the world, since every elaborate object is an open system with its own unique history of development. At the same time the personal trajectories for two sufficiently approximated objects should be close on the field of evolution, or at least sharing the same global attractors.

The most important contribution of synergetics to modern science is the introduction of a new class of processes: the appearance of complicated regular structures out of primary unordered systems after they achieve a certain level of complication. Gradually developing and increasing in complication, a system can jump to a new, more organized level.

This transfer has the character of a bifurcational jump—an abrupt change of state. A good example would be the freezing of water, when the unorganized liquid turns into a regular crystal. There are many similar processes all around us.

Of course, it is impossible to present all ideas of synergy in brief. Our aim here is to give only the main impression. The best way to introduce any new complicated concept is to illustrate it with simple examples. It is traditional for books on synergy to bring in Benar's cells of boiling liquid or the baker's transformations. Migrating from book to book, these examples are clear and illustrative, but only for specialists. At the same time, synergy claims to be one of the most general views on the surrounding world, so there must be numerous exemplary instances scattered around us and waiting to be identified. Let us turn again to the magnificent world of mountains, which has been so inspiring in providing the authors with so many instances during this study.

Let us imagine a flat glacier somewhere up on the mountain. The snow covers its surface with an even white layer. The wind blows and covers the snow with a dark dust from surrounding rocks (Fig.3.5a). As a result, there appears a layer on the surface of the glacier which is a quasi-homogeneous mixture of dark particles and white snow grains (Fig.3.5b).

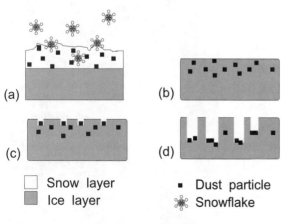

Snow layer     ▪ Dust particle
Ice layer     ✳ Snowflake

*Fig. 3.5. Formation of quasi- regular structures in Nature*

When the sun comes out, the dark particles close to the surface become heated. The snow around them starts to melt (Fig.3.5c), the particles melt their way inward, forming small craters. Where there are several particles close together, the process proceeds faster. In this manner there appear bigger and bigger craters, separated by icy saddles and peaks (Fig.3.5d). The bottom of the craters is paved with dark particles that get heated more and more intensively, compared to higher parts, with crater walls forming a kind of lenses. Smaller irregularities disappear due to the absorption by bigger ones.

Under certain conditions (the distribution of particles' sizes, their concentration, the thickness of layers, the sun's intensity etc.) a regular structure of icy pillars could appear. This structure is called *calgaspory* or "ice of penitents", since it resembles a crowd of praying monks. Any mountaineer has encountered it in more or less clear form (Fig. 3.6). The process is a very typical synergetic process in the still nature. It shows very clearly that synergetics is not a creation of a new physics, but a recognition of new sequences and connections of our well-known old world. In this sense the mountain glacier is a very good "firing gild" for the study of synergetic ideas. Every winter it is covered again with fresh new white snow, which gradually crystallizes into new ice. The sun then rises, and in the springtime its shine, the stones fallen from rock walls, the water and the movement of the glacier itself turn its surface into an exhibition of bizarre architectural forms.

Here you can also encounter "ice mushrooms" (Fig.3.7), small rivers and valleys, towers and tunnels. All these components could be regarded as a cumulative effect of many different causes, resulting in the appearance of complicated natural forms. In some abstract single case it can be strictly calculated when the stone would sink deep down in the ice and when it would built up an icy table. It can be explained how the water, running over the flat surface of the glacier, makes riverbeds and caverns. It can be shown how the same material—water—has different properties at the same time: mobility of fluid, softness of snow mass, fragility and daintiness of snowflakes, crystal hardness of ice. All these forms become each other and affect each other simultaneously, in full accordance with synergetic representations.

*Fig. 3.6. Examples of regular formations in the mountains.*

*Fig. 3.7. Examples of regular formations in the mountains*

The application of approaches, developed within the framework of the theory of dynamic systems, to human sciences such as biology, sociology, and biochemistry proved to be very effective. One can expect the same results from the application of the synergetic paradigm.

## 3.3. Biological Applications of Synergetics

For the purposes of further discussion let us study some basic biological principles through the synergetic approach.

It is known that biological evolution is based upon natural selection, acting through the mechanisms of (1) variation—the appearance of mutant forms, (2) selection of useful attributes, (3) inheritance of selected attributes, or signs.

Let us label the fact of appearance and selection of a sign $a$ on a certain step $k$ of evolution as $a_k$. An organism involved in an evolutionary process and described by the whole set of signs $a_i$ will be referred to as $A_k$. Then it is possible to denote the fact that the organism acquire a sign $a$ on the step $k$ as follows:

$$A_k=\{a_k,A_{k-1}\}$$

Obviously, we can inductively open this succession of signs acquisition as

$$A_k=\{a_k,A_{k-1}\}=\{a_k,\{a_{k-1},A_{k-2}\}\}=\{a_k,\{a_{k-1},\{a_{k-2},A_{k-3}\}\}\}\ etc.$$

This equation may be interpreted very clearly: it proves the absolute necessity for any organism to have an evolutionary memory. Introduced in several publications as a hypothesis or a postulate, this statement is a mandatory property of an accepted evolution mechanism.

A deducible consequence of this statement is the presence of a certain program of the organism development. This program can be represented by a succession of steps:

$$a_k,a_{k-1},a_{k-2},...,a_0 \qquad\qquad (1).$$

Let us stress again that we do not employ the existence of a memory and a program of organism's development to explain evolution. Quite the contrary: assuming the existence of an evolution mechanism, we deduce the inevitability of the memory and the genesis program. At this stage we are not interested in the investigation of the exact form of this program.

Every element $a_i$ of the program fixes one of many possible bifurcational directions of development for an individual organism, determining the movement of the system to a new attractor. Generally, the development program (1) could be regarded as a chain of transfers from an attractor to another attractor. The discussed sense of "attractor" concept explains a relative insensibility of the system's movement from $a_{k-1}$ to $a_k$ for small influences and disturbances.

The existence of this program makes an organism on the verge of embryogenesis "run through" all previous stages of development $A_k$, $A_{k-1}$ ... of the species to which the organism belongs. Even when at a modern stage a more or less optimal decision is discovered (for example, *Homo Sapiens*), the evolution in principle has no other ways to reach this decision "faster" than through the execution of already formed program. This fact is a logical consequence of assumed statements, but at the same time it can be regarded as proof of reasoning. This fact is very well illustrated by the stages of embryogenesis. The *Homo Sapiens* embryo in its development passes through all the stages of different biological forms (Fig.3.8).

At every step of evolution the appearance of a sign is connected with the influence of the environment. The appearance and disappearance of gills, the tail, the development of eyes and the brain eventually—all is determined by

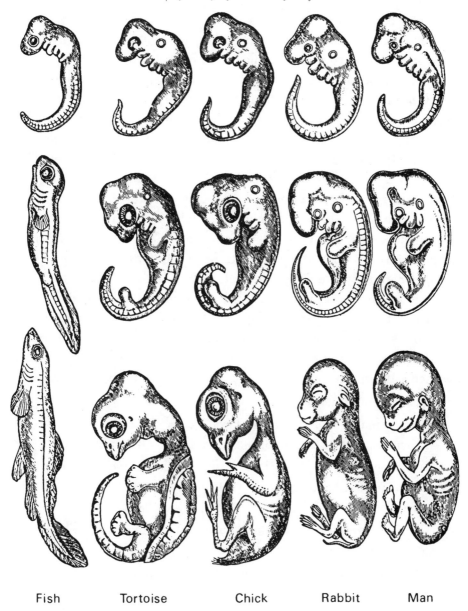

| Fish | Tortoise | Chick | Rabbit | Man |

*Fig. 3.8. Stages of development of a Homo Sapiens embryo*

environment. We should stress that environment is an outer universe for an individual organism, not only for the species in general (even the density of population of the species could affect the individual organism). The cosmic cataclysms long passed also left their marks in a form of loops and deviations of the program.

It is obvious, that the 'tail end' of the program defines certain starting conditions for the beginning of the goal-seeking procedure. If the environment changed so that these conditions could not be compensated by any new signs $a_{k+1}$ to keep the solution in an acceptable range, the species ceases to exist.

Certain simplest organisms under the conditions of present and past environment turn out to be in the state of balance. There is no necessity to select any new signs and the program lingers at a certain step $n$. By the same reasoning, different steps $a_k$ reflect different periods of 'virtual' time. The transfer from $a_{k-1}$ to $a_k$ can be a reflection of billion years of evolution and is performed in the embryo within one week, while another transformation between $a_{n-1}$ and $a_n$ reflects million years and takes a month.

In the end it is interesting to note that a question of the first element $a_0$ of the program (1) is very closely tied with Anthropic Cosmological principle, very popular around the middle of the century in cosmology. It states that "The Universe must have those properties which allow life to develop within it at the same stage in its history." [Barrow, Tipler, 1986]. In other words, the existence of humans is possible only under a certain combination of fundamental constants, chosen from infinite set of values. If but one constant were different, the existence of organic life in the Universe would have been impossible.

Let us make several conclusions.

1. The acceptance of evolutionary laws logically implies the existence of a memory and a program of the genesis of any individual organism.
2. This program provides the information needed to transform from one global attractor to another global attractor in the process of development.
3. The program is formed by the influence of the environment with a goal of species survival.
4. The program is not the fastest way to a local optimum, it contains the whole process of goal-searching.
5. The program indirectly describes the development of the environment and the history of a species adapting to it.

Whatever the form of representation of the genetic program, there should be some specific tools and mechanisms to be controlled by this program. It is not enough to know that a certain organ should be developed (for example, an eye), but there should be also some instructions how to do it and where to put it (the eye should not be placed inside the armpit). It is quite obvious, that the mechanisms and the basic principles of their operation should "comprehend" the 3D structure of the universe. To ignite and control the process of cell differentiation into a specific organ, the initial cell must "know" not only the current stage of the executing program, but also its exact location in environment, i.e. possess the information on 3-D space structures both built and to be built.

It is clear that electrical or chemical, as well as any other "isotropic" mechanisms alone cannot be responsible for this phenomena. Inevitably there should be a spatial structure with some singularities along coordinate axes. The best candidate for this role could be a field of some kind.

Let us note a very interesting result: Many different studies in rather mutually distant branches of knowledge in the long run meet at one single point: the study of biological fields. So in the next section we will discuss the current state of this problem and express some new ideas.

## Summary.

1. Synergetics has made a very important step ahead: from the study of idealized (simple) systems to the study of more realistic (more complicated) systems. These open dissipative systems exchange energy and information with the surrounding universe and are far away from any balance point.

2. The study of these systems cannot only provide an explanation for several pivotal physical paradoxes, but also provide a new conceptualization of the world.

3. The ideas of synergetics are very helpful in the description of different phenomena in the nature around us, both still and alive.

4. Coupled with the classical postulates of Darwinism, the principles of synergetics inevitably drive us to several important conclusions. One of them is the logical necessity of the existence of memory and program for the biological objects' development and its close connections to the whole development of life on Earth.

5. This development is not smooth (evolutional) only, but consists of several bifurcational jumps. Every jump leads a biological species to a new state.

6. It is clear that electrical, chemical, or any other "isotropic" mechanisms alone cannot be responsible for these phenomena. Inevitably, there should be some spatial structure with some singularities along coordinates. The best candidate for this role could be a field of some kind.

# 4 Biological objects emission. Spin-Torsion Fields: one of the carriers of biological information?

*"Our remedies oft in ourselves do lie
Which we ascribe to heaven"*
William Shakespeare, *"All's Well That Ends Well"*

It is generally known that, among other properties, the biological cell is a generator of a wide spectrum of oscillations. As academician V.P.Kaznatcheev states (1991) "Many years of study of super-subtle emission in cells and tissues of living organisms drive us to a conclusion that living cells emit quanta of electromagnetic field. We can assume that for a living cell the emission is an essential manifestation of its vividness, i.e. we speak of specific electromagnetic fields. For the cell itself they form an internal system of information exchange, without which the life of the cell is impossible."

For the cell structures this phenomenon was experimentally discovered in the first quarter of our century by A.G.Gurvitsch (1922) and further studied by V.P.Kaznatcheev and L.P.Michaylova (1981). It was shown that super-subtle *emission of photons* is peculiar to the majority of bio-systems, excluding some types of algae and bacteria. According to the perceptions dominant at the time, the main role has been assigned to the electromagnetic waveband.

In the mid-60's, V.P.Kaznatcheev developed a theory that the *electromagnetic field quanta* can be regarded as one of the most important material carriers of information flows in biological systems. It is possible that super-subtle emissions of quanta are responsible for general control of all exchange processes in the cell . Bio-systems could respond to external inputs with reactions, providing the amplification, damping or accumulation of the electromagnetic signals. Cells and cell-populations operate as specifically organized devices, emitting and accepting photons both from external space and "internal virtual" photons, produced in the course of accepting matter-and-energy flows of external media. Kaznatcheev has put forth a concept of the biosphere as an "unbalanced photon constellation (an ensemble)", existing only via incoming external energy. This constellation provides "the communications between the cells, needed for coexistence of protein-nucleotide structures. The quantum information is stored inside the molecular structures of cell constellations".

On the other hand, the whole development of life on Earth falls under intensive cosmic influence and is structured by the cosmic matrix. It would be too bold to discuss how it shapes the concrete forms of life, since we are only in the beginning of a protracted direction of study.

It is possible that the role of this omnipresent matrix is performed by *relict radiation.This radiation appeared at the moment of 'separation' of emission from matter some 300,000 years after the 'Big Bang'.*

The remarkable discovery of relict emission determined the development of modern cosmological representations. The *relict emission* has an astonishingly high isotropy. This fact allows us to use this emission as a basic coordinate system and to measure the velocity of the movements of the Earth, Solar System, and our galaxy in relation to this emission. The relict emission has another unique property: its spectrum exactly coincides with that of an absolutely black body, i.e. has Planck's distribution of wavelengths. The explanation is that in the first stages of Universe development there was a balance of matter and emission. In the process of universe expansion, the temperature decreased, but the spectrum character remained the same. It was both before the separation of emission from matter and after that cosmic emission experienced the last dispersion of matter; the Universe started to become transparent and nothing affected its spectrum any longer. Today the spectral distribution of the relict emission reaches the millimeter waveband (which corresponds 2.7°K). The relict emission reaches the surface of the Earth but the high-frequency part of the spectrum is strongly absorbed by the atmosphere. For the whole history of atmosphere and organic life of the Earth there have not occurred any significant shifts of wavelength distribution's peak.

It is worth mentioning the effect of weak (informational) influence on acupuncture points by the EMW of millimeter waveband. It can be assumed that the function of the relict emission as super-stable cosmic substance is a "fine adjustment" of the organic life by low-frequency part of its spectrum. The high-frequency part of the relict emission spectrum apparently has no direct effect on the organic life. At least it should have much more subtle influence. Incidentally, the absorption of this part of the spectrum is reduced in the mountains. That may be the explanation why it is recommended that we "communicate" with the cosmos there.

We now have reasons to assume that, in addition to electromagnetic waves, the cells have emissions of another physical nature. This idea was well expressed by Vernadsky:

*"Around us, inside us, here, there and everywhere, without a break, always changing, coinciding and colliding, pass emissions of different wavelengths—from the waves of 1/10,000 mm length up to long waves, measured by kilometers. All space is filled with it. It is very difficult—perhaps even impossible—to comprehend this medium, the medium, of the world we are living in, where in the same place we can distinguish always new kinds of emissions, as our research techniques get progressively better. They are changing eternally, they are filling continuously the whole universe, and this feature distinguishes sharply the matter-less cosmos from the ideal space of geometry. The stuff of biosphere is soaked with energy, it becomes active, it collects and distributes within the biosphere the energy accepted in the form of emission, and transforms it eventually in the geosphere into a free one, able to produce work"* (Vernadsky, 1989).

Very attractive appears to be the theory of *torsion fields*, developed and experimentally proved by the Moscow group of scientists headed by E. Akimov [Akimov, Moskovskii 1992]. They claim that along with curvature the space-time geometry also admits the property of torsion, and with it particular torsion fields. The concept of torsion fields is widely known in modern theoretical physics.

The properties of the torsion fields are quite unique: the potential of a torsion source is independent of distance; the torsion fields generated by spinning objects feature axial symmetry; the group speed of torsion waves is much greater than that of light and its lower boundary is estimated as $10^9 c$; torsion radiation is not attenuated (screened) when passing through natural media; the spin-polarized media generates stable spin (torsion) phantoms owing to the spin-torsion interactions; and all organic and inorganic objects have their own characteristic torsion fields. (The critical point of these speculations was the claim that, in contrast to the case of *spinning source without radiation*, for a spinning source *with* radiation the theory does not require that the constant of spin-torsion interactions be necessarily small.) Consideration of spin systems of living organisms provides a sufficiently substantiated explanation for many psycho-physical phenomena. The concept of the *brain* as a spin prism of a kind is an interesting outcome of the studies. The brain was represented as a spin torsion system of non-magnetic nature. Here, the brain is simultaneously a torsion receiver and transmitter.

The reality of these phenomena implies interaction between intangible and tangible objects. Obviously, the carrier of this interaction must have both tangible and intangible properties, and also be a real-world object. It is precisely the torsion fields of complex configurations that seem to satisfy these conditions. By virtue of non-linearity of torsion field equations for sources with radiation, a part of torsion field configurations appearing during the reflection of ideas prove to be stable and to exist independently as torsion phantoms, that is, objects that are both tangible and intangible. Existing industrial sources (generators) of torsion radiation have made it possible to investigate the effect of static torsion fields and wave torsion radiation on various physical, chemical, and biological objects, as well as to simulate some psycho-physical phenomena.

The unusual properties of torsion fields, which follow theoretical considerations and have been confirmed experimentally, give rise to the hope that this concept can be very useful in understanding the psycho-physical phenomena, but at the same time one should clearly understand that the torsion field (if all the claims mentioned above are real) is only a part of a wide spectrum of biological object emissions. It occupies practically the entire range of radiation: from ultraviolet to infrared and other wavebands of electromagnetic waves. All these emissions carry some information about the biological object.

Actually, in this study we do not attempt to specify the waveband to which the biological object oscillations belong, whether electromagnetic, ultrasonic or torsion. It is only important at this stage that a cell emits a wide spectrum of waves, which in principle can be described by a generalized set of frequencies, phases and amplitudes. Each of these parameters depends on time and varies within a very wide range.

## Summary.

1. The influence of *EM field* on the development and functioning of biological objects is confirmed by many experimental data. Very important are different forms of cosmic emission. Interesting speculations arise when comparing the parameters of relict emission with the basic biological frequencies. The new, yet undiscovered emission wavebands cannot be excluded from the realm possibility.

2. A very attractive possibility seems to be the new concept of torsion fields, generated by spin-effects of elementary structures of matter. Current studies claim these field to have very specific features and properties. When correctly proven, these torsion fields could be regarded as principal material carriers of the biological fields in nature.

# 5 The transfer from a cell to a biological system

*"One touch of nature makes the whole world kin"*
*William Shakespeare, "Troilus and Cressida"*

It has been shown in many works that when cells build up to a certain biological system, their corporate behavior starts to diverge from the behavior of any single member. We can find examples in yeast suspension, a microorganism colony or any complicated biological object. It can be assumed that one of the most probable explanations for the observed distinction is the mutual synchronization of emissions of all constitutional cells.

A widely known example is synchronization of clock pendulums attached to a moving support bar. After a certain time, all the clocks mounted on the bar begin to run absolutely synchronously. This illustrates the resonance synchronization principle. For the advance of resonance it is necessary to have an interconnection of system elements through which the synchro-references are propagated. In the case of a mechanical system, such as clocks, this reference is the mechanic impact, delivered from one clock to another through a common underlay. In the case of electronic systems the reference is the electromagnetic pulse.

In the case of biological systems it makes sense, on our opinion, to connect this interaction with information transferred from one part of the system to another. The carrier of this information is the emission we mentioned earlier.

It is necessary to clarify what we understand by the concept of "resonance synchronization," as applied to a biological system. In many cases the sharp resonance in its strict mathematical sense for large systems or cell ensembles is rather improbable. It is more correct to speak of a coordinated behavior, or the fact that all these elements have one and the same attractor. A very close analogue could be a concept of the forced resonance, when the system's frequency floats around the resonance one but does not coincide with it.

So we come to the conclusion that a necessary condition for the synchronization (or correlation) of a different processes in a biological organism is the exchange of information between different organs and systems of this organism.

At the same time it is accepted now that a necessary condition for biological existence is the receiving of information from the outer space, in particular from the Sun and planets. A.L.Tchizevsky and V.I.Vernadsky can be named as founders of this direction of studies. They have produced massive factual material demonstrating the connection between the living stuff of the planet with the cosmic radiation flows. From the modern point of view it is clear that together with the energy we get from the cosmos comes information—since all emissions from the outer space are not chaotic quantum streams, but rather structured messages that influence our organisms and determine their existence and development. Later we will return to the character of their structure.

Any kind of resonance interference or holographic phenomena imposes a strong restriction: the rigid synchronization of the oscillations. If the mechanisms responsible for this synchronization remains unexplained, if the fundamental reasons for its appearance and maintenance remain concealed, any theory would be forced. Moreover, the existence not only of phenotypic, but also genotypic synchronization require explanation of repeatability and inheritance of this feature.

Let us recall that protein synthesis is performed in accordance with the information contained in the *DNA* specific to the protein. All four types of monomers—nucleotides— building up this polymer, have their own unique 3-dimensional structure. In accordance with the principles developed in this study, they have their own unique field structure, too. The codons (triplets of nucleotides, defining the succession of amino-acids in every protein) build up an alphabet for every organism's code and also have their own characteristic field structure.

A stable 3-D structure is connected with every 64 possible code units of a plant, animal or bacteria (and with every amino-acid accordingly). Even very mutually distant biological forms have similar fragments of DNA chains. For example, the hemoglobin of a dog has only 16% of the code fragments' replacements, as compared with a man's hemoglobin. This unity and the very restricted set of components that build up all 'living material' provide necessary preconditions for the appearance of a natural resonance synchronization.

The complementary foundations in the two-chain molecule of DNA could be regarded both as a reason and as a consequence of the resonant synchronization phenomena, since the concrete physical effects building a foundation for the 'executive mechanisms' like replication and transcription remain unknown.

The same considerations can be applied to the process of synthesis of a specific protein in ribosomes. The protein chain, generated link by link, simultaneously forms its wave image, its unique synchronized field portrait. Accordingly, the synthesis via the "biochemical machine" resonance image builds out from the components of lower levels.

The unity of the protein structure and, furthermore, of all cell material in the process of multiplication and differentiation stipulates a likely resonance synchronization on higher levels.

This process can be looked at from another angle. When biological cells constitute a system, and when this system overcomes a certain level of complexity, it acquires a principally new property: an explosive bifurcation process of self-organization starts to form. From a set of independent cells it transforms into a cell ensemble, interacting with surrounding space as a whole entity. This transformation has the character of a leap and, since the system under study is an open one, it can be described in accordance with synergetic principles. The system transfers to a new level of organization; due to energy and information exchange with the surrounding media in the system there starts the process of entropy deterioration—or, as is more often said now, of producing a *neg-entropy*.

The inevitability of resonance in complex systems can be proven from the most common point of view. To do so we should return to synergetics again. Synergetics is not only a new field of science, but an entirely new (for Western thinking) vision of nature and all its processes ranging from pure mechanics to biology and social patterns. The importance of synergetics is gaining wide acceptance in the scientific community. The synergetic approach spreads widely into different fields of human knowledge. At this stage, analogy is the most effective modus operandi for establishing this new paradigm. One should transfer the perceptions and techniques well proven in one field of knowledge to other fields, to be substantiated later. Let us introduce an analogy connected to the objective of our study, based upon the works of I. Prigogine.

Western scientific thought is based on mechanics. The triumph of Sir Isaak Newton's theory empowered scientists to question the composition of the universe, and open the door to its study. The key statement of Newton's mechanics is $F=ma$, i.e. the definition of proportion between the moving force and the acceleration of the body. The main achievement of the theory is the ability to evaluate the movement of interacting bodies using this formula and its derivations. Newton's law is constant with respect to time $t$: variables do not change when $t$ is substituted by $-t$. Newton's laws are reversible and deterministic: knowing the initial position and velocity of a body, one can always find its velocity and position at any particular moment.

For more than three hundred years scientists have believed the world to be built in accordance with Newton's mechanics, to be predictable and reconstructible: if a trajectory leads from a point A to B, the same trajectory leads from B to A. Problems that could not been solved through mechanics were regarded as temporary obstacles. Everybody knows, of course, that it is much easier to evaluate the trajectory of a falling stone than the trajectory of three moving bodies, say Sun, Earth and Jupiter. But the latter still was considered computable and causing just a technical difficulty.

Later this opinion turned out to be wrong, or, actually, not quite correct. The starting momentum for developing new representations was provided by a theorem proven more than one hundred years ago by a French mathematician Jules Henri Poincaré. In a simplified way Poincaré's concept could be described as follows: could mutual influence between dynamic systems be excluded? Systems that allowed this exclusion were called *integratable*. Systems of this kind are isomorphic with the systems of free particles. The simplest form of equations describing the movement of a system allows integration, i.e. explicit evaluation of their trajectories. All dynamic systems described in the primary scientific textbooks are integratable. The problem of two bodies belongs to this class of systems.

However, for the majority of dynamic systems the answer to Poincaré question was negative. In the fundamental theorem, proven in 1889, Poincaré showed that generally dynamic systems cannot be integrated—the interactions cannot be excluded.

The principal significance of Poincaré work for us is that it revealed the reason why dynamic systems cannot be integrated and the interactions excluded: occurrence of resonance.

Resonance can be described as an energy transfer between two connected periodical processes with equal or multiple frequencies. Poincaré showed that in the attempt to exclude the influences, the resonance caused a divergence of solutions: the dynamic expressions for the solutions had members with denominators such as $(n_1\omega_1+n_2\omega_2)$. At the points of resonance $n_1\omega_1+n_2\omega_2=0$ and numerators are divided by zero, accordingly. The solution approaches infinity. But the appearance of infinity in a physical equation is a sign of a singular situation!

Poincaré also showed that there is no way out of this dead-end: the problem of small denominators belongs to the number of principally unsolvable problems of dynamics. In the beginning, the results of Poincaré's studies aroused the interest only among specialists. The majority of physicists were inclined to see this problem as a purely technical one, which would be eventually successfully overcome by sufficiently clever mathematics. The situation changed abruptly in the mid-50's, when it was shown that resonance leads to two types of trajectories: the first are trajectories with *normal behavior,* well-known through the study of two-bodies problem. The second are trajectories with *stochastic behavior.* The development of these representations brought to life the concept of so called *Big Poincaré systems,* in which resonance plays a very important role.

As an example, we can mention the interaction between a particle and a field, studied by Prigogine. The latter can be regarded as a superposition of oscillators with a continuum of frequencies $\omega_k$. A particle performs an oscillation with a frequency $\omega_1$. We are facing the example of *non-integratable Poincaré system.* The resonance would occur any time when $\omega_k=1$. It is well known that emission of radiation is caused by this kind of resonance. The emission is a non-reversible process explained by Poincaré resonance. New feature appears when the frequency $k$ is a non-discrete function of index $k$. This is a peculiarity of Big Poincaré systems, i.e. chaotic systems, having only stochastic trajectories. Big Poincaré systems reflect many important physical situations.

In effect, they reflect majority of situations in nature. But Big Poincaré systems also allow one to bypass Poincaré's divergence, i.e. remove the main obstacle against the integration of the system. This result destroys the determinism and reversibility of Newton's and Hamilton's mechanics, since the solutions for Big Poincaré systems generally are statistical and non-symmetrical in time.

Prigogine's school of thought made another big step. It proved clearly that there is a remarkable correspondence between the problems of classical theory and those of quantum mechanics. Hence Poincaré's proposed division of all systems into integrable and non-integrable remains valid for quantum mechanics as well. The central link in Prigogine's chain of reasoning is the concept of *quantum chaos*—chaos in a mathematical sense.

In classical dynamics the idea of chaos appears when studying the systems sensitive to initial conditions. Let us consider the reflection of the light. It is well known that for a light beam the angle of incidence is equal to the angle of reflection. If a focused beam strikes a flat surface, the reflected beam comes through a certain point (Fig.3.9). Let us shift the striking beam by a small angle. The reflected beam will move by the same angle. With fluctuations of the striking beam within narrow limitations the reflected beam will stay inside a small cone. Let us take a case when the beam is reflected by a convex surface. Fluctuation within the same angle will cause dramatic consequences: the reflected beam will move far from the previous area. The reflection comes to be chaotic (Fig.3.9d).

This simple example illustrates the meaning of the classical concept of chaos: neighboring trajectories diverge. Prigogine showed that evolution of these systems can be described only in terms of stochastic ensembles. That means that the set of equations does not describe a particular trajectory or a particular wave-function, but rather a family of them. Those systems are called chaotic by Prigogine. This definition is applicable both for classical and quantum systems. It is important that under this consideration the fundamental Newton or Shröedinger equations are valid, but for a limited class of systems, i.e. the old theories are included in the new one.

The developed approach made it possible to deduce many fundamental sequences. Prigogine has shown the irreversibility of time in the description of physical systems. It was done through the introduction of chronological structuring of events. For stable dynamic systems the solutions for the movement equations are symmetrical in time. Unstable dynamic systems' solutions remain symmetrical, but there appear two families of solutions with non-symmetry in time. The disappearance of symmetry is a very important step in the solution of the time paradox: nature is much less symmetrical than one could expect from the equations of classical and quantum mechanics.

Non-reversibility and probability are two organic attributes of the world described by Prigogine. Prigogine's group has developed a stage of main progress of the physics; they started a new coil of science evolution spiral. The solution for a range of principal paradoxes brought physics back to natural perceptions, helped get rid of subjective and outdated considerations. At the same time these views are closely tied with ancient perceptions of the world, keeping a 'golden middle' between rigid determination and voluntary anarchy.

The success of developed concepts creates a challenge to apply them to many other areas far away from theoretical physics. It seems to be very promising to try the concept in humanist sciences, starting from cytology and physiology to sociology of group behavior. Roughly speaking, the behavior of any group described by a generalized group function cannot be reduced to the behavior of a single member of this group. That is the consequence of resonance, which is a necessary condition for the existence of open systems integrating with the surrounding world.

Let us recall the concept introduced by Jahn [Jahn 1988] of the quantum nature of consciousness. In the framework of this concept consciousness should be regarded as an open dissipative system and the whole apparatus developed by Prigogine can be applied to it. Once again the leading role in the behavior of the system should be played by resonance interactions—both among the elements and with other systems of the kind.

Summing up, we can assume that in biological systems the transfer to the next level of organization is accompanied by resonance synchronization of cell radiation. This leads us to the first postulate of the introductory model.

*The main condition of functioning of any complex biological system is the cell resonance synchronization. This synchronization is provided both by the internal synchronizing references, i.e. the references coming from the other parts of the system, and by external references.*

## Summary.

1. The transfer from the group of individual cells to the level of a complex organism has a character of bifurcational self-organization: the properties of the organism cannot be defined as the sum of properties of the composing elements.

2. The clockwork reason for this self-organization is the process of resonance synchronization of separate system's elements.

3. On one hand, the synchronization possibility could be explained by the unity of the genetic structure of biological objects. On the other hand, the theory of dynamic systems predicts resonance for interacting systems with close natural frequencies.

4. The interaction between different components of a complicated biological systems (e.g., cells) can be described as information exchange through fields and emissions.

# 6 The holographic universe — a new understanding of old ideas.

*In the holographic domain, each organism represents in some manner the universe, and each portion of the universe represents in some manner the organism within it.*
K. Pribram

The concept of universe as a whole and man as a part of this whole must be the most ancient idea of human wisdom, stated in all ancient sacral texts. The concepts, accepting inspiration as a general property of the world, have roots in ancient animism and in some way can be traced in any ancient civilization. Elements of these views can be found in ancient Greek philosophy. The idea of general inspiration of the Universe is one of the central perceptions of Egyptian, Babylonian, Indian, and Chinese cultures.

For example, in sacral books of ancient India—Vedas, generally dated to 1500 BC, there is a whole range of gods representing the different powers of the cosmos. But all these gods are recognized to be the names and forms of the one Being (ekam sat), who has no name and no form. That is a basic Hindu doctrine. In the Vedic vision there are three worlds: the physical, the psychological and the spiritual. The whole universe was seen to be one, but manifested at three interwoven levels. In Rig Veda one can find a description of giant Cosmic original man — Purusha —whose parts formed the universe. His ears developed into the sun, from his navel appeared air, from his head—sky, from his feet—Earth etc.

Similar representations one could find in Chinese myth of pangu, recorded in III-IV century A.C. In accordance with the ancient Chinese views, between the two main powers (Heaven and Earth) there is a third one—the Man. The verge between living and still nature in the Chinese nature philosophy is very uncertain. Everything is spirited and full of life. There is no cardinal difference between the world and a man. A man is not opposed to the world, he is the part of the world and, in the end, the world itself. The ideal pursued by Chinese wise men was the natural man in the state of harmony with the world and following live rhythms of nature. Different structural levels of cosmos were regarded by the ancient people as one organism, whose parts built up a harmonic ensemble.

From about AD 500 to AD 1500, the so-called *perennial philosophy* spread throughout the civilized world, both west and east. It was found in China as a development of Taoism and Confucianism which came to a head as the *neo-Confucianism* of the 17<sup>th</sup> and 18<sup>th</sup> centuries; in India as the development of *Vedanta*; in the rest of Asia as *Mahayana Buddhism*; in Islam as both the philosophical development of *Islam* and as *Sufism*; and in Europe as the medieval Christianity. The core of these universal wisdoms was the idea that the material world was pervaded by, and would find its explanation in, a transcendent reality. This transcendent reality was known in China as the Tao, in Mahayana Buddhism as the Void, the *Sunyata*, in Hinduism as the *Brahman*, in Islam as *al Haqq*, the Reality, and in Christianity as the *Supreme Being*. The development of these ideas and their meaning for the modern world are discussed in Bede Griffiths [Griffiths 1992) book.

During the mechanistic era (17<sup>th</sup>-18<sup>th</sup> centuries) this philosophy began to be gradually undermined in Europe. The new materialistic philosophy, supported by tremendous scientific achievements, began to emerge, coming to a head in the 19<sup>th</sup> century. Materialism has become a major component of our everyday life, and most of our attitudes to life were determined, at least unconsciously, by a materialistic view of reality.

20<sup>th</sup> century passed under the sign of the great revolution in physics, the perception of the limitations of Newtonian-Cartesian model and mechanistic approach to the universe in general. However strange, this approach is still used when studying psychological processes and the role and place of consciousness in the world around us, notwithstanding the fact that many scientists pointed out its limitations. New perceptions are being formed gradually, based on the accumulation of data and ideas. After a certain point, the social consciousness is to jump to a new pattern of thinking (See [Ho, 1993; Gribbin, 1995; Laszlo, 1996]).

The undertaken study shows that a biological system could be regarded as a complex-structure set of field emission sources, synchronized by frequencies and phases. Sources of this kind are called *coherent sources*.

It is known that a simultaneous application of the fields by coherent sources forms an interference pattern in space. In the same way, we can assume that a certain field structure is attached to any biological object. This structure is principally 3-dimensional (let us recall that well-known holograms are projections of similar structures in optical waveband on the plane of photo material). The 3D structures like that can be formed not only in optical, but in any other spectral waveband. That gives us the foundation to postulate that the functioning of any complicated biological system is accompanied by interferential interaction of coherent field emissions of separate elements, constituting the system *per se*. For any stable biological system this structure is quasi-stationary, i.e. it relatively slowly changes with time and preserves its configuration within a coordinate system attached to the object.

There is nothing especially new in this concept. In the end of 70's a specialist in theoretical physics D. Bohm, and a specialist in neurophysiology K. Pribram introduced the concept of a universal, cosmic hologram, or *holoversuum* [Bohm,1980; Pribram,1981]. This concept caused a broad response in the science world. It dealt with the integrity of the universe, whose indivisible parts are humans and consciousness. The connections between them were defined as a universal informational and field hologram, determined by the specific features of the system organization of the human brain.

Pribram assumed that this 'parallel functioning' is of mandatory importance for the organization of brain activity, and the interaction of these two systems results in the appearance of new wave phenomena, in full accordance with holographic principles.

These ideas were enthusiastically adopted by parapsychology. This is how it is expressed in the book "Quantum Questions" [Wilber 1984]:

*"Psychic phenomena are only byproducts of the simultaneous-omnipresent matrix. Individual brains are bits of the greater hologram. They have access under certain circumstances to all the information in the total system. Synchronicity ... also fits in with the holographic model. Such meaningful coincidences derive from the purposeful, patterned, organizing nature of the matrix. Psychokinesis, mind affecting matter, may be a natural result of interaction at the primary level. The holographic model resolves one long-standing riddle of psi: the inability of instrumentation to track the apparent energy transfer in telepathy, healing, clairvoyance. If these events occur in a dimension transcending time and space, there is no need for energy to travel from here to there".*

## Summary.

1. The idea of the holistic Universe was often the subject of ancient theories. The concept provides that there are many different manifestations of the same substance of the Universe. An important consequence is the unity of all structures and of the ways of development.

2. These perceptions have been revived by modern science in the form of the holographic principle of the universe's structure, including biological objects and human brain.

3. The resonance synchronization of all involved structures leads to the appearance of an interferential spatial structure with certain holographic properties.

4. This structure is the biological field for which we have been looking for a long time.

5. Rather than identify the concrete wavebands or frequencies of emissions, it is of more importance to understand the specific character of this structure and to recognize its unique properties.

# Chakra system and acupuncture channels.

*"How long a time lies in one little world!"*
William Shakespeare, *"Richard III"*

The introduced concept of organism interferential field can be applied to explain different aspects of its existence [Korotkov, 1995a] and, primarily, in order to understand the process of embryo development.

We can assume, in accordance with the introduced approach, that all cell population centers transforming into different organs of an organism, are involved in the process of resonance synchronization. These centers can be responsible for the whole development of an organism from the stage of fertilized cell, explaining the 'executive mechanism' of the differentiation process. In order to start at a certain place of a would-be embryo's process of differentiation into cells of specific organs, the initial cell structures must "know" their exact location, i.e. posses 3-dimensional spatial information. As was mentioned above, it is clear that no electrochemical or any other isotropic mechanism can be responsible for this phenomena.

The field structures are 3-dimensional, so they provide a conceptual physical basis for the explanation of how 'a plan' of embryo's development works. The assumption is that at every stage all field structures are involved in the process of structuring of the cell population in order to build up certain organs of the organism. Though changing in the course of organism development, the same structures survive through the total life-cycle of the individual organism.

It can proceed as follows: at the first stage of embryogenesis there is a population of little-differentiated cells formed by division from the fertilized egg. They form a simple spherical field and spherical physical structure

(Fig.3.10a) and are involved in mutual resonance synchronization. At the same time this structure experiences the influence of external structuring field of the mother. The interference of these two fields provides the orientation in the 3-dimensional space for the whole stages of development. In other words, the mother's field provides a specific coordinate system for the 'assembly' of the embryo (Fig.3.10b). At the next stage of development the process of sub-differentiation can happen at any place of the sphere, due to space symmetry of the structure, but the external mother's field defines an axis in the space, reducing the number of freedom degrees for the location of next sub-populations. After a certain step the space orientation and all topological peculiarities are defined by interconnection of the non-symmetrical field of an embryo and the mother's field (Fig.3.10c,d). Sometimes the space orientation can occur without the mother's field. In that case the primary cell ensemble has only to define its own axis of symmetry in space. This could be orientation in accordance with the external geo-cosmic fields. At this stage of the study it is very difficult to draw a border between the structural effects of the embryo field itself and the mother's field. (The example of a hen laying eggs and the success of incubators illustrates the difficulty of this separation). Maybe this pre-orientation in space is important only for the species with inter-womb development of the embryo; maybe it takes place at the very beginning stages.

In the process of development the embryo inevitably will create resonance centers, imposing the character of the oscillations on the

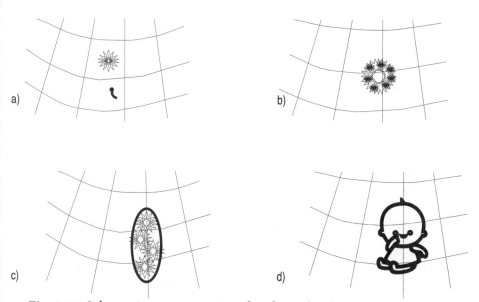

*Fig. 3.10. Schematic representation of embryo development in mother's field*

neighboring cell structures. Due to the necessity of very fine structuring and tuning of the different subsystems to different resonance frequencies, there could be several centers of the kind.

Such perception of these primary development centers very well complies with a concept of *Chakras*, known by many ancient representations. Chakras can be regarded as external manifestation, generalized 'traces' of the most important resonance centers of a biological object. Consequently, their role is not restricted to obsolete appearance. They are designated not only for development, but for operation and "maintenance" of separate organs, as well as for coordination of activity of a group of organs. In accordance with our perceptions, all field structures of the chakras are well synchronized with each other.

Next assumption is that the contemplated field structure could be directly tied with the system of acupuncture points and channels. Many years of study failed to find a specific nature of these points. From the point of view of this hypothesis it becomes clear: these points are not mutated cells or tissues, as they always were thought to be, but only projections on the skin surface of the nodes of 3-dimensional field structure. For instance, they could be the projections of the standing wavefront's extremes [Zhang, 1996].

There are several consequences derived from the postulate of holographic character of the biological objects' field, which apply for any kind of sufficiently complicated biological system. Though acupuncture points are discovered both in animals and in plants, for our convenience we will proceed to address only human aspects.

**Consequence 1.** A biological object could have more than one 3-dimensional topological field structure; in principle—*ad libidum*. That is, there can be many different systems of acupuncture points and channels of one organism. This consequence is justified by the existing concept: there is a classical Chinese system of acupuncture points and channels, there is an Indian system of energy centers—chakras, there are recently developed systems after Foll, Nakatani, Su-Jock.

**Consequence 2.** The main features of a certain field structure can be discovered in any small part of it, which is well proven by the acupuncture practice. It is well known that practically all points can also be found in the ear, in the eye iris, on the hand, leg etc. In principle, it is possible to take almost any area of the skin and there find all the points corresponding to all systems and organs. But the smaller the area, the worse the resolution. This principle is the basis for the holistic approach to understanding the Universe, which naturally belongs to the sacral philosophy of the ancient East.

**Consequence 3.** The studied field structure is principally 3-dimensional and therefore is not limited to the body's confines, spreading far beyond its surface. Here we come to the idea of multi-layer aura, so popular both in eastern and western esoteric schools.

**Consequence 4.** This structure is principally boundless and exists in the whole universe, but the resolution fidelity decreases with distance. It explains the possibility of diagnostic and remote influence on the object. This structure possesses virtually complete information about the object generating the field, and by this information it is possible to reconstruct the structure of the object. This principle is very widely used by the modern holography. The same idea can help us understand the phenomenon of telepathy without attracting any material carrier. To establish contact it is necessary to synchronize the 3-dimensional field structure of the recipient with that of the inductor. A detailed study of this synchronization needs a special contemplation.

# Summary.

1. The individual bio-field of an organism is formed as the result of gradual cell structuring process in the course of embryogenesis. A side-effect of this process is the appearance of a system of resonance centers.

2. The main centers of the kind could be tied with the concept of chakras, widely used by many ancient theories.

3. The whole system of the resonance centers can be coupled with the idea of acupuncture channels and points. One explanation can be that they are but a projection of the structure on the surface of the body (skin), which explains the absence of any specific morphological elements.

4. Any kind of influence on the points, from pins to super-high frequency or laser emission, would lead to the same results on the whole field structure of the organism.

5. The same principles enable us to assume the existence of the structure in the whole universe at the same time. Any point of the Universe contains the whole information on any single object, but at a resolution decreasing with distance.

6. The bio-field of any person spreads without any limitation all over the universe, but needs very sharp resonance tuning for its identification.

# 8 The energy-and-information structure of an organism.

*"The Greeks were much too sensible to think in terms of either-or. For them, it was always not-only-but-also. Not only Plato and Aristotle, but also the maenads... All we've done is taken a leaf out of the old Greek book."*
Aldous Huxley, "Island"

Now we can define the notion of *Energy-and-Information Structure* (EIS) of the organism. By this term we understand the structure of the organism together with all its connections and influences. The idea is illustrated by Fig. 3.11. We take into consideration the exchange of energy and information both with the upper and the lower levels. The carriers of this energy and information may be tangible objects and physical fields, consumed, excreted, absorbed, and radiated by an organism on different levels of its activity. It is essential that in this notion the interrelations and interactions between the parts of the system are of equal importance as its physical properties and manifestations. Organism here is a part of environment, both tangible and informational.

That is a reflection of an already discussed fact, that the human being is an open dissipative system, which is being changed by the environment and changes the environment itself. This particular fact forces us to regard all the parts of the system discussed above and their manifestations as very flexible, changeable, developing, and not rigid or fixed. Let us return to the example discussed above and present some new ones.

For many centuries scientists have been arguing: what features of the organism are more important—inherited or acquired ones? In other words: is there an initial, primary difference between an English lord and an Australian aboriginal?

This dispute is not purely academic: different points of view resulted not only in the development of different systems of education and printing of many thick books, they formed a basis for developing racial and racist theories, as well as their practical applications.

The question was always put in the *either/or* form (for example, "*either* Darwin *or* Lamarck"). It was very important for the western world to assign a priority, to put a certain trend above all others. Let us refer to it as the *either/or principle* from here on. Another approach could be called *both/and principle*.

In the given example that would mean that everything is important for the developing of the organism: the genetic set inherited from the parents, the anamnesys of the embryonic stage of development (the food consumed by the mother, the music she listened to, emotions experienced, the character of delivery process etc.), circumstances in which the child was bred and educated. Only the compound of all these factors will result in the formation of a specific human organism with all its characteristics.

Naturally, at every step one factor or another will prevail, very often defining the remaining course of life. For example, if a pregnant woman is affected by radioactivity, the result can be a child's defective organism. If an offspring of an English aristocrat happens to fall into a family of monkeys in his formative years, regretfully he will not become a Tarzan, but only a human-like ape. Still, the poor animal might have a lean aristocratic face, due to the genes.

All factors work as a complex. One can probably regard the newborn child as a cupboard with different shelves for different abilities: a shelf for mathematics, a shelf for sense of humor, a shelf for music etc. Right after birth the shelves are empty, but their sizes are significantly different from person to person.

Further, the environment will help fill these shelves, but no more than they could contain. Of two students attending the same musical school, one will perform at weddings and another will become Mozart. But if this potential Mozart is born in a medieval African tribe, the maximum he could achieve is virtuosity at the slit drum.

The *'both/and'* principle is fully applicable to the whole living activity of any organism. For example, the condition of its existence is to support a homeostasis with surrounding media through the consumption of food, air, sun and water. A lack of any microelement in the food (iron, for example) will cause disease and, eventually, death. But, on first look, this microelement exists in the body in minuscule quantities!

Another example: a rat is kept in a cage (with optimal living conditions inside) for quite a long time. At some point, another cage is placed next to it. In this cage a happy couple of rats enjoy an active sexual life. The poor animal in the first cage will inescapably lose its appetite and weight and, in some extreme cases, may even be killed by the stress. In other words, for a biological being any influencing factors can turn out to be significant. One cannot say a-priori, which one would be dominant.

For any concrete situation, all significant factors could be categorized by the degree of their influence. For example, factors affecting a person's state:
- lethal factors (hit by a car);
- directly affecting the physical state (freezing);

- indirectly affecting the physical state (lack of sun);
- stress factors (unrequited love);
- informational factors (cholesterol level warning).

This list can be continued. Moreover, any categorization of the kind reflects a particular aspect of influences. For example, the factors determining the genesis of a child in the first month of its life can range as follows:

- genetic information;
- pregnancy history and conditions;
- character of delivery;
- information fields;
- astrological situation; etc.

The main idea is that any complicatedly organized biological being exists in direct contact with the whole surrounding world. Every aspect in this world plays an important role. Changing even the most insignificant factor can bring sufficient alterations to the life of the whole population, up to its disappearance. Naturally, the higher the adaptability and the easier a species can change its behavior in accordance with the changing environment, the higher its chances of survival. One could compare, say, a small population of koala bears which feed on very particular plants, with gray rats which can endure radiation and high-voltage electric current, eat everything, and multiply like brush-fire.

Attempts to find the place for informational factors in this kaleidoscope of the changing hierarchy of factors seem to be unreasonable. At this stage it is important just to prove their existence and understand that they determine—in many aspects—the whole life of any being, including the human being.

The introduced definition of EIS of the human being focuses on the interaction of a particular organism with surrounding world. Every single person is treated as an elementary field particle. That means that this object can be regarded as a wave under some circumstances and as a particle under others.

Tangible and non-tangible worlds are no longer separated—we are leaving Descartes' limitations and coming back to the ancient perception of an integral world, but on a new coil of the spiral of scientific knowledge. Physical body and consciousness are but different facets of the same phenomenon. For some processes the former is more important, for others—the latter, but still they are one and the same essence. This essence turns out to be directly connected to the whole universe.

The introduced concept is a theoretical foundation for the study of EIS distortions. By the EIS distortions we understand the faults in the system of relations between the organism and the environment leading to disturbances of the organism's media and, eventually, to the development of pathological processes. Through this we are approaching the study of the nature of diseases, but this falls beyond the scope of the current study.

The external manifestation of EIS is the distribution of field structures of the organism, which can be identified through the spectrum of components: electrical field, magnetic field, thermal field and so on. We personally consider as very promising the visualization of EIS through *Kirlian Effect*, since it is an integrated, multi-factor parameter.

## Summary.

1. The concept of EIS of the organism is introduced as a multilevel system in its interactions with surrounding universe and environment, in the unity of physical fields, radiated and absorbed by the organism, and information signals, significant for its life-support activity.

2. The definition is based on the perception of multi-level hierarchy of the structure both of the organism, and of the factors influencing its development and existence.

3. At any particular case all the factors can be divided into horizontal levels (different effects on the same classes of objects) and vertical ones (interaction between the objects of different levels).

4. There is no sense to speak of the contradiction between the tangible and the non-tangible: they are but different manifestations of the same reality.

# 9 Structural synchronization in a group of organisms

*"Strong reasons make strong actions."*
*William Shakespeare, "King John"*

We have introduced the main principles of the functioning of an organism as a biological system. Here we will address a group of organisms creating a new system, since all above-mentioned considerations are applicable to this group.

Every single organism of the group is described by its own emissions with a specific set of frequencies and phases, and under conditions of synchronization they form a new common system with its own field structure.

All postulates and sequences introduced above are valid for this structure too. This structure is the next level of organization in relation to a single person. This structure is formed by the emissions of the systems of a lower level, and at the same time it sends its own synchro-signals to each of them. All people, regardless of sex, race, or age have a principally similar field structure: the structure of energy channels. This fact was identified already in ancient China and is confirmed by modern and most delicate instrumental research.

Naturally, this structure is in a way a simplification or generalization. For different people it will vary depending on the person's, but *statistically* it can be reproduced with high accuracy. Consequently, some groups of people can form their own unified topological field structure. In accordance with the principle of holography, the resulting structure would resemble every individual's structure.

According to the introduced principles, a stable structure of every next level can appear only when resonance synchronization has occurred on the next level below, i.e. in this case on the level of individual person. This first level includes small formations of people. In practice, synchronization on this level can be identified as deep interpersonal connections such as love, hatred, parent-child relations, sibling relations, true friendship etc.(Fig.3.12).

With its structure being formed, every next emerging system loses its independence and becomes a cell of the field structure of a higher hierarchical level. The next level of structuring is the level of ethnicity, i.e. a group of people, unified by the same territory, religion, language and traditions. As a field structure of a person is unique, so is the individual field structure of every ethnicity.

This is the *spirit of a nation*, for thousands of years discussed by philosophers and historians. The introduced model shows that this spirit is a real structure in the

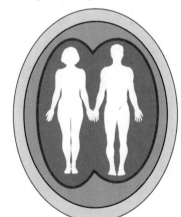

*Fig. 3.12. United field of two synchronized*

universe, having its own properties and peculiarities. These properties, as was discussed above, could be observed in every element of the structure, i.e. in every single person of the ethnicity.

Eventually, there is a level of the whole mankind that forms its own structure in the universe and smoothly flows into the level of Cosmic Con-

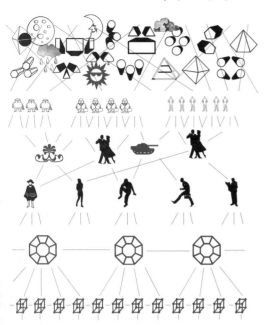

*Fig. 3.13. Schematic levels of interconnections in the universe*

sciousness. These structures are boundless, they are spread all throughout the Universe, interfering and interacting with each other (Fig.3.13). Apparently, specific regular grids (recorded by the modern bi-olocation techniques—dowsing, e.g. the Kerr grids) can also be regarded as a manifestation of these structures.

It is clear now that the elimination of a certain amount of elements would not affect the operation of the system, provided that informational signals of the remaining elements are sufficient for the maintenance of the resonance synchronization of all elements constituting the system. When this condition is not observed, a more or less significant distortion of EIS occurs. In its turn, it induces a distortion of information signals from upper levels to lower ones and, accordingly, the malfunctioning of the weakest elements of this lower level.

Another important sequence of the discussed postulates is a concept of a *critical creative mass*. That means that a creative activity can exist only when a sufficiently large part of the intellectually active population form their own structure and their information matrix accordingly. The creative activity in this sense is regarded as the generation of certain ideas, interaction between these ideas and information matrix, amplification, and multiple reflection of those ideas. This factor explains simultaneous occurrence of new ideas to different researchers in the different places, which many times was observed in the history of science.

It makes quite apparent the necessity of the emergence of big cities and their role as scientific and cultural centers. The intensity of informational field in the cities is especially high and its influence on the intellectual activity of the people covered by this field is very strong. This is how new ideas grow and spread. In other cases ideas die away, even when introduced from the highest level. This happened to the idea of monotheism, brought by pharaoh Ekhnaton, or the flying apparatus invented by Leonardo da Vinci. At the same time, small tribal groups cannot build groups sufficiently large and stable to support the advanced field of consciousness.

There is a natural objection: how does one explain the existence of hermits? Why had all the great thinkers always gone off into solitary existence to form their big ideas? The answer can be naturally derived from the introduced hypotheses: the field of collective consciousness constructs and amplifies new ideas, but at the same time it introduces its own limitations. New ideas often turn out to be a part or development of already existing concepts, i.e. a part of existing paradigm formed at this level of structuring. The person feels the approaching of a new idea or, in other words, 'anticipates' the possibility of contact with another level of structuring. He should completely free himself of the current level's fields influence—only then can he verbalize new ideas, while further development of these ideas and their structuring of the consciousness field can only happen in a big group.

Moses, Christ, and Mohammed had all gone to the desert for isolation and meditation, but came back to preach among their compatriots. These ideas, however revolutionary, were shaped in traditional form, and remained connected to the previous paradigm and presented as their development.

From this point of view we get a clear sense of existence of every human being. This question always has been a challenge for philosophers, since the majority of people have to answer it at least at the end of their life.

Every man is an elemental cell, a primary source of EIS of his nation and, additionally, of the whole mankind. Without these primary cells the appearance and existence of the structure is not possible: when a critical mass of cells is destroyed, the structure is destroyed too. One can find an analogy with eritrothids: fluctuations of their number within narrow limits does not affect the state of the organism, but a break beyond the borders initiates a pathological process. So, every single person should be proud of his existence, since he contributes to the existence and development of the whole mankind.

The other remarkable notion is that a person, by the account of his creative activity, can contribute to the Universal Information Field. Ideas, carefully elaborated and nourished, can generate stable phantom images, which gain their own independent momentum independently. 'Ideas fly with the wind'. This statement applies to technical discoveries and also to the spiritual evolution of mankind. Let us demonstrate this definition with an example.

About 800 BC in ancient India, the *Aranyakas* (the Forest Book) was created. It was the turning point for the history of India and, to some extent, for the history of the whole world. The great break from the ancient mythological, ritualistic religion to the discovery of the inner self has occurred. This happened when the *rishis* (or seers) stopped offering sacrifices to the external fire. They retired to forests for meditation in order to ignite the inner fire.

A new psychology emerged, along with a new understanding of the human and the universe. This emergence occurred in the Upanishads, but it took place also in Sakyamuni Buddha practically simultaneously. Nearly at the same time Heraclitus and other Greek philosophers were studying *logos* (the mind) as the basis of the universe, while the Hebrew prophets, Isaiah, Jeremiah and Ezekiel, discovered the reality of the transcendent God. And in China, a new concept was to be created as well. This was a key period in human history, and practically all religions today stem from this great experience of the fifth and sixth centuries before Christ.

It is necessary to emphasize the complex character of the concept of Information Field as we understand it. It includes not only continuous field structure of information patterns and images, but also more traditional forms of communication and information exchange. It can be illustrated by the following table, although due to the discussed principles, one can make allowances for the conventional and artificial character of this structure.

- Space-Field Form-Images
- Global Information Networks
- TV Networks
- Radio Networks
- Newspapers
- Books
- Special professional papers
- Software, including play-soft
- Films, including video
- Oral information exchange
- Private correspondence

We could find another foundation for this classification (for example, the type of information carrier, the perceptive organs etc.), but it is of no importance. The main thing is to understand the idea of significance of all particular forms and their mutual influence.

A good example of information resonance is the progression of achievements in sports. Many past records have now become the norm for less

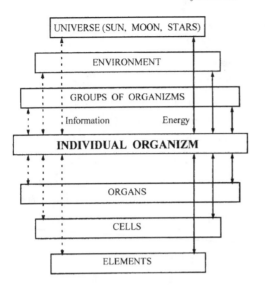

*Fig. 3.11. Energy-And-Information structure of the organism*

than accomplished sportsmen. In 1786 Balmat and Paccard reached the summit of Mont Blanc. It was a climax of more than 26 years of attempts to conquer the biggest mountain of Europe. Year by year afterward, the number of people ascending it grew higher and higher. Now, about 50-80 hikers climb it every day in summer-time. Is it the ability of people that developed over the two centuries? Let us study this phenomenon in more detail.

Assume that there is a certain number of people going in for a special sport, say, high jumping. Somewhere, a trainer appears who has invented a new approach for training. One of his pupils wins a local district competition time and time again. The new approach spreads among a small group of trainers and sportsmen. One of the most talented, using this technique, reaches outstanding results and wins a world championship. The approach is widely studied, which leads to an increase in the general level of skill.

In following years the approach is improved through psychological assistance. The new champion together with his psychologist write a book, explaining the details of the new approach. During the competitions many films are shot. Soon the new approach becomes common. This evolution process from time to time is broken with a jump of results due to the invention of a new style.

Fig.3.14 shows the dynamics of World records in high jumping. As can be seen from this picture, the records of this century grew by 50 cm, considerably overriding the growth of the sportsmen's height. It is necessary to point out, that the line on the picture has very few horizontal stretches. This indicates that the relay race of records has continued on and on, and always there was a sportsman to improve the achievement of a seemingly invincible champion. A very demonstrative example is one of V. Brumel, whose last record of 228 cm held from 1968 to 1971, when further progress was started by

Furthburry, who invented a new style of high-jumping. It is interesting, that Furthburry won the Olympic Games of 1968 in Mexico with 224 cm, which was considerably lower than Brumel's record.

The same pattern can be traced for many other sports. This clearly shows: the reason is not a mutation of Homo Sapiens as a species, since anthropological parameters for the corresponding period of time have not changed significantly. The reason is the information resonance discussed above.

We can find another clear example in education. In medieval Europe, only the noblemen and monks passed the knowledge from generation to generation. Decade by decade the number of educated people grew, until an explosion occurred. The technological revolution demanded a mass of educated people, and a very interesting fact became clear: in medieval times it took many years to learn how to read and write, not even to mention mathematics. In our society, a six-years-old child can do it in one year. Once again, it is not a biological evolution, but an influence of information field of a society.

At this stage of our study the differences between introduced approach and morphogenetic field of Sheldrake can be clearly seen.

We introduce into consideration an additional formative element: the structural field of the species. It is formed by the species itself and develops along with its evolution. In other words, the structural field of every biological species emerges due to the activity of its representative samples. That is why Darwin's evolution theory remains valid as well as the theory of genetic transmissions. This approach renders redundant the introduction of primary form—*eidos*. The evolution of biological world goes gradually along a more and more complicated spiral. Also there is no need to invoke the hypothesis of the Cosmic Impact or Cosmic Visitors.

## Summary.

1. Resonance synchronization in the group of organisms leads to the appearance of a common field structure. The new structure is the result of the '*synergetic summation*' of all individual structures.

2. The common structure is formed by individual contributions, but at the same time it affects each of its individual elements. This influence can be explained by the synchronization information signals' spreading.

3. One can speak of the existence of the *information field*, directly connected with the group structure, when the group consciousness is

structured by socially important ideas. The ideas are amplified and get new interpretations due to collective resonance.

4. Any intellectual development is possible only when there is a sufficiently large number of people who can comprehend the ideas and resonantly propagate them in the media for further amplification.

# 10 The hierarchy of synchronization levels.

*"Every subject's duty is the king's,*
*but every subject's soul is his own"*
*William Shakespeare, "Henry V"*

Let us stress a very important point. As shown above, we can speak in terms of *matter-and-information structure* of our world. The *matter* is represented by substances that have both physical (that we can feel) and informational (that we can comprehend) nature. Matter substances are organized in a hierarchy of systems; the systems of lower levels are subsystems to the higher levels. We know only a part of this hierarchy. For a biological beings the levels will be as follows.

a) cell

b) gene

c) intra-organism (individual organs, tissues)

d) biological organism as a whole

e) group of organisms, united and mutually synergized
   (population)

f) big groups of organisms (exosystem)

g) biosphere

Every individual element of any level is able to generate specific signals. When interacting, these signals can become amplified or attenuated and form the unified information signal, in its turn affecting the structures of lower and higher levels. Those signals are not designated to be informational, they merely accompany the activity of life. Still, they carry information that can be retrieved by a motivated receiver of any level. It is reasonable to assume that synchronized signals of different levels are characterized by different generalized frequencies. Consequently, the propagation of the signals between levels can be asymmetrical: the influence will go down easier than up.

The hierarchy introduced above is based on the approach to the *tangible* aspect of live nature. According to the *hierarchy* and *block principles* discussed earlier, we can propose another hierarchy, based on the information activity, i.e. the activity responsible for forming the organism information signals. The first level under consideration is the level of functional organization, i.e. the level at which the different tasks of organism's self-support are solved.

- the functional level of *inter-organism systems* (breathing system, digestion system, blood system etc.). All the systems of this level are correlated and synchronized with each other, exchanging information signals and sending signals up to the—higher levels.

- the level of *reflexive subconscious behavior* of humans and animals, responsible for the functioning of the organism as a whole entity, as one biological system. On this level, the information and energy exchange with outer media very important. Signals of this level are responsible for acts of everyday life. All the decisions of life-support are made at this level, but are directed and prepared by the signals of higher and lower levels. For instance, no animal would start searching for water if it is not thirsty, i.e. if there is no signal from the physiological receptors.

- the level of *Isotropic Collective Consciousness*, the level where every element is only a particle, practically identical to each other and able to live only as part of the system. This level would include the blood system with blood particles as elements, an anthill, a beehive. The information can be carried both by chemical agents and by fields.

- the level of *Elementary Individual Consciousness*, i.e. the simplest brain work, not connected directly to physiological needs but derived from them. This level can be observed in humans and higher-level animals' behavior. Examples of decisions made at this level are: storing up reserves of food for the future, building shelters before the coming cold etc.

- the level of *Complex Individual Consciousness*, connected with the rational construction of images, with the logical analysis and predictions of situations. This activity can be seen mainly in humans. It defines the current functioning. This activity is an auxiliary and servile one for the survival of the individual and the species in whole, and the signals from this level define greatly the existence of simple collective structures of higher levels.

. the level of *strong emotional activity*. In the process of this activity a strong information field can be generated, able to influence other people, structuring them and inducing them to behave in unison. This is a level of love, strong attachment, wisdom, and leadership. This level is responsible for the operation of *non-functional structures* and collective field networks. By the non-functional structures we understand quasi-stationary patterns like duty, honor, platonic love, etc., contradicting rational functional behavior.

. the level of *Anisotropic Collective Consciousness* systems, generated by individual persons. This is a level of Collective networks—structures like political parties, unions, and religious and military institutions. These structures have their own level of synchronizing signals, which can be corresponded with the concept of the collective unconscious in Jung's interpretation.

. the level of *Cosmic Consciousness*

Eventually, we can speak of meta-level of synchronization, relating to the propagation of signals not between adjoining levels, but directly from higher levels. This phenomenon is responsible for the processes like 'intuitive' creation both in art and science, creative and religious revelations, contacts with a 'higher mind', healing and other paranormal effects. All levels influence each other and are mutually dependent. Affecting one of them indirectly affects all.

## Summary.

1. There can be identified several levels of resonance synchronization of the spatial field structures. The informational synchronization signals spread in all directions between all levels.

2. This phenomenon leads to the formation of structures similar to collective distributed networks, which have both tangible and non-tangible components.

# 11 Human consciousness after death: a new view

*"The dread of something after death—
the undiscover'd country
from whose bourn no traveler returns"*
            William Shakespeare, "Hamlet"

The ideas introduced in this part of the study enable us to return back to the main question of this book: what happens to a person after death? What was it that we registered in these experiments? We have described a person as the unity of a material body and an EIS. The latter has the following main properties:

- 3-Dimensionality, existence in the whole space simultaneously (but with different resolution);
- The presence of tangible and informational components;
- Instant propagation;
- Virtual absence of screening effects;
- Embodiment as a part of higher structures, mutually affected through energy and information exchange; Individuality for every person, but patterned by the information field of parents, family, society;
- Quasi-stable existence in time-space.

Now we can put the same question in a different form: Does an individual EIS exist after the death of its physical body and, if the answer is positive, for how long?

At this stage we can make only general assumptions. As was shown above, EIS of a person is formed through the interaction with EIS of environment and society, structuring the space by the mere fact of its existence. The stronger and more active a person is, the stronger his influence on the whole structure, and the more distortion the structure experiences due to the peculiarities of this person.

This can be seen most clearly on the examples of famous statesmen, thinkers, writers etc. The personality of Alexander the Great in the beginning has structured the Greek city-state, the whole Asian city-state later and ended up in cultural integration of a big part of the contemporary civilized world. It is another issue that he turned out to be the ideal resonator, the ideal receiver of the ideas already developed in the ancient world and just waiting to be implemented. That alone has made his mission so successful.

Another example is Napoleon. While he reflected a collective idea, while he remained in resonance with the collective information field, he was accompanied by success and luck. When he put personal interests above the interests of the nation, when his own ambitions came into contradiction with the interests of the majority, then his EIS felt into dissonance with the structure of the society and he was defeated.

So we can assume that during the lifetime of every single man the total external EIS field is being locally distorted by him. This external field is like a mold, enwrapping the field of a person and can be regarded as an EIS phantom of the person.

This phantom is a certain quasi-stable formation, lingering for some time after the death or physical absence of this master person in a given point of space. Phantoms can be attached to certain material objects, certainly to the body of a dead person, his personal belongings, places where he lived etc. That can serve as an explanation for ghosts of the dead, poltergeists and spirits.

This phantom is a certain measure of how the collective information structure is distorted by a given person. The bigger this distortion, the longer it exists, and the more closely it is tied to the special features of a particular person as it spreads to a larger number of people.

On the other hand, this distortion can be represented by a certain resulting peak in the information field. When 'the information frequency' of a particular person coincides with the generalized frequency of a large group of people, a high resonance peak can be observed. The amplitude of this peak very roughly can be estimated by the number of people involved in this resonance.

The appearance of the peak is connected with the activity of a concrete person, but later it could exist independently from its owner, i.e. make a phantom of a *soliton type* (single wave).

So we can say that phantoms of Napoleon or Alexander the Great have been leading a stable existence long after the death of their originals, and are even presented now, though blurred with time.

We can introduce the concept of characteristic lifetime $T_L$ of a phantom after the death. This parameter depends on the degree of field distortion caused by the person during his life. In other words, $T_L$ is defined by the number of people involved in the scope of a person's activity and the degree of this involvement.

For the estimation of $T_L$ let us assume that a person directly affected every $K^{th}$ person out of a population of $N$, i.e. a total of $N/K$ people. In the next generation, he would affect every $K^{th}$ person out of $N/K$, i.e. $N/K^2$, and so on.

The last generation *m* still experiencing this influence will be the generation where at least one person is influenced, i.e. $N/K^m \geq 1$, $N/K^{m+1} < 1$. Let us set $T_L = m$.

Hence $N = K^{T_L}$ and

Hence $T_L = \log N / \log K$

Of course, this formula is but a rough estimation for $T_L$, but it helps to understand its meaning. So, for a Robinson Crusoe, who spent his life on an uninhabited island, $T_L = 0$, in relation to the European world. Napoleon influenced $10^7$ people and his influence was very strong (say, every second person would remembers him).

$T_{L Napoleon} = 7/\log 2 = 23$

So, at least 23 generations will remember Napoleon in the European world. Vidal Sassoon influenced practically the same amount of people, but his influence is much lower.

$T_{L Sassoon} = 7/\log 1,000 = 2.3$

Let us stress that the discussed phantom appears not only in a limited time period, but also in a restricted space domain. For example, Mr. Crusoe, thrown ashore on an island inhabited by tribesmen, disappears from the information universe of his country. For England, in this case, his $T_L = 0$, but for the islanders he can be the founder of a new culture, new traditions and habits, and become supreme ruler. He can structure the information field of this island and his phantom would exist decades after decades. One can recall the legends of white rulers who helped Cortez conquer Thenothetlan.

One can object that the above is not directly related to life after death, but is rather a collection of memories. Let us once again lead your attention to the fact that the proposed model postulates the unity of the tangible and the intangible. They represent two facets of the same reality and are internally inseparable. A thought is as real and valuable in this world as a hammer or a stone. The imprinted distortion of the field caused by a person's existence smoothly blurs and disappears, but asymptotically lasts forever.

Very closely tied with the phantom concept is the idea of *reincarnation*. As we mentioned above, the phantoms of concrete people can exist long after their death in a certain area of time-space. They are distorted and blurred with time, but the possibility cannot be excluded that these phantoms take part in the formation of a new human being. Later, their traces can appear as reincarnation reminiscences.

Let us remark, that these reminiscences appear either in a childhood or in altered states of consciousness—by the influence of psychedelics, hypnosis, meditation. These states facilitate the connection to the information field, identification of these components and their translation from one level of sub-consciousness to another. Once connected to a structure, it is much easier to reproduce this state, reestablish the once-experienced resonance. That is a basic principle of occult training.

It is well known that mentally disturbed patients frequently identify themselves with another person, i.e. they are totally structured by an alien information field. In this case their own structure is totally replaced by a phantom. Naturally, more often it is a strong phantom of Hitler, Stalin or Napoleon, than a phantom of a dishwasher John. The classical concept of reincarnation does not provide that Stalin can be reincarnated in one thousand people, while John in one or even none. The introduced perception states, that the number of resonances with a single phantom is not limited. It might be that the understanding of this process can later result in discovering new ways to heal patients with mental illness.

> *"When Jesus "came to the other side", to the country of Gadarenes, two demons met him, coming out of the tombs, so fierce that no one could pass that way.... Now a herd of many swine was feeding at some distance from them. And the demons begged him, "If you cast us out, send us away into the herd of swine." And he said to them, "Go." So they came out and went into the swine; and behold, the whole herd rushed down the steep bank into the sea, and perished in the waters." [Matt.8.28,30-32].*

Can we not tell that Jesus just restructured the phantom from one biological carrier to another— maybe it will be a promising direction of study in the nearest future?

One can see, that the introduced concept is totally different from the Oriental reincarnation idea as a linear chain of linked lives. At the same time, our considerations show that a built-in phantom can influence a person's EIS, determining both the physical and the mental state. So the idea of karma still exists, but in a different interpretation. In this sense karma is the projection of a dominating phantom and/or of phantom's components on the psychological plane of consciousness.

On the other hand, karma can be regarded as a system of global attractors, including the final one, existing at the moment of birth. As was discussed above, this succession can be altered by the outer world and, to a smaller extent, by the person himself.

If we go back to phantoms, the same idea may be expressed in another way. If there is a structuring, there could be a *restructuring*, i.e. one can get rid of harmful acquired structures which is the goal of EIS correction. But this subject falls beyond the scope of this study.

## Summary.

1. The Energy/Information Structure of a person is formed through the interaction with Energy/Information Structure of environment and society, structuring the space by the mere fact of its existence. The stronger and more active a man, the stronger his influence on the whole structure, and the bigger the distortion the structure experiences due to the peculiarities of this person. During the lifetime of every single person the total external information field is being locally distorted by him.

2. This external field is like a mold enwrapping the field of a person; the fields can be regarded as the information phantom of the person. This phantom is a certain quasi-stable formation, lingering for some time after the death or physical absence of this person in a given point of space. This phantom is a certain measure of how the collective information structure is distorted by a given person. The bigger the distortion and the longer it persists, the more closely it is tied to the special features of a particular man, spreading to a wider number of people.

3. On the other hand, this distortion can be represented by a certain resulting peak in the information field. The appearance of the peak is connected with the activity of a concrete person, but later it can exist independently from its owner, i.e. make a phantom of a soliton type (single wave).

# Conclusion

*"His ideal was pure experimental science at one end of the spectrum, and pure experimental mysticism at the other. Direct experience on every level and then clear, rational statements about those experiences."*
Aldous Huxley. "Island"

The biological and informational universes are but different sides of the same reality, and the concept of evolution is fully applicable to the information world as well.

In this particular world Homo Sapiens is dramatically different from the other biological beings. The speed of Homo Sapiens' development is much higher than of any other species. Practically without biological change, the mankind as a species made tremendous progress in their information world, leaving far behind the seemingly more adaptable, powerful and promising competitors. Due to the evolution in the information world, the Man has captured not only a leading, but a dominating position. Correspondingly, he has changed biological world and environment.

That is a very important point: whatever happens in the information universe is of the same importance to what happens in the physical world.

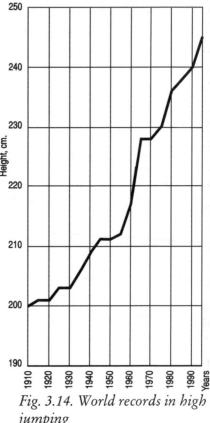

Fig. 3.14. World records in high jumping

As was discussed above, the main properties of the Energy-and-Information Universe, as well as physical world, are based upon wave interaction in many different ways. If a concept such as the one introduced in this study is to be proven experimentally, appropriate instruments should be developed through relevant areas of technical sciences.

Experimental data shows that Kirlian photos of any parts of a human body (living or dead) do not contradict the proposed model. In addition, the specific features of the Kirlian-based technique (which meanwhile is the most sensitive for the study of EIS) makes it nearly the only tool available today.

Of course, this should not stop attempts to find other adequate instruments. This task is very complicated, since the nature of emission, wavebands, information modulations and intensity is concealed.

It is quite natural and we can give an example in order to illustrate it. Let us imagine, that a certain alien automated probe from the distant cosmos scans the surface of our planet. It would discover absolutely abnormal activity in millimeter waveband (which is explained, as we know, by TV broadcasting). This activity, not ceasing for a moment, still has some peaks, immediately after the observed location is moving out of sunlight (as we know, there are more channels on the air in the evening time). Some areas of the Earth surface have a higher density of this emission. The aliens do not know what the destination of these waves is, they are not aware of the specific characteristics of TV signals and devices for its deciphering. They regard this emission as a specific information sign. Through a very elaborate study they can discover that there are several kinds of those signals (different TV systems, different channels). As they cannot come close to the surface and have no information sources but their space-probe, they cannot guess the existence of surface-based, localized systems for signal generation and globally distributed satellite systems. In the end, the alien scientists would conclude that the Earth is a specific being, whose activity can be registered in the corresponding waveband. One can only imagine what a concept of the inner structure of this being could be put forth, and what program of the study would be developed. They will never arrive at the idea of mankind without sending a new, more sophisticated probe.

In a way we are in the same position: we are in the beginning of a very long exploration of Energy-Information world. One of the main objectives of this study was to find a way to apply the western scientific paradigm to the investigation of the world, traditionally studied in esoteric ways. The approach provides several steps: the acquisition of facts unexplained by modern science, proposal of a hypothesis, experimental verification, and refinement of it into a theory.

Not only should the theory itself have all the traditional attributes of the western paradigm, but similar principles should be observed at every stage of this development. Among them, the first to be mentioned are experiment repeatability, objectivity and independent reproducibility.

In the times of great geographical discoveries, navigators had always brought along their maps, much like navigators of today. Looking at the older maps now, we can only be astonished: how could they achieve such great results in their voyages with such primitive prior knowledge! Our study can be regarded as such a primitive, perhaps naive attempt to map out the great expedition toward knowledge.

# Bibliography

Agni Yoga. 1992. Moscow (in Russian).

Antonii Arkhiyepiskop. 1953.*Chto My Mozhem Znat' o Zagrobnoy Zhizni Dushi Cheloveka.* (What Can We Know About the Life of Man's Soul Beyond the Grave). Russkoye Vozrozhdeniye, v.24. New York. (in Russian)

Aries, Philippe. 1985, *Images of Man and Death,* Harvard U. Press, Cambridge, Mass.

Aries, Philippe. 1992. *Chelovek Pered Litsom Smerti.* [Man Confronting Death]. Moscow. (in Russian)

Berdiayev, N.A. 1991.*Problema Cheloveka.* [A Problem of Mankind]. Stupeni, v.1. (in Russian)

Blavatsky, E.P. 1993.*Razoblachennaya Isida.* [Isis Unveiled]. Moscow. (in Russian)

Bulgakov, S. 1935. *Zhizn' za Grobom.* [Life Beyond the Coffin]. Paris. (in Russian)

Bulgakov, S.N. 1992.*Gheroizm i Podvizhnichestvo.* [Heroism and Self-Sacrifice]. Moscow. (in Russian)

Bulgakov, S.N. 1993. *Ot Marksizma k Idealizmu.* [From Marxism to Idealism]. Moscow. (in Russian)

Fedorov, N.F. 1982.*Sochineniya.* [Essays]. Moscow. (in Russian)

*Figury Tanatosa.* [The Forms of Thanatos], 1991, 1992, 1993.Almanac of Philosophy. St. Petersburg. (in Russian)

Govinda, Anagarika Lama. 1060. Introductory Foreword. in *The Tibetian Book of the Dead.* Oxford. NY.

Grof, S. 1985. *Beyond the Brain.* State University of New York Press.

Grof, S. 1993.*Za Predelami Mozga.* [Beyond the Brain]. Moscow. (Russian translation)

Gurevich, A.Ya., 1989. *Kultura i Obshchestvo Srednevekovoi Yevropy Glazami Sovremmennikov.* [Culture and Society of Medieval Europe through the Eyes of Contemporaries]. Moscow. (in Russian)

Hancock, Graham. 1995. *Fingerprints of the God.* Mandarin, GB.

Jung, C.G. 1960. Psychological Commentary in *The Tibetian Book of the Dead.* Oxford. NY.

Kalinovskiy, P. 1991.*Perekhod.* [Transition]. Moscow. (in Russian)

Kubler-Ross, E. 1992.*Smerti Net.* [Death Does Not Exist. Moscow. (in Russian)

Kubler-Ross, E. 1977. *Death Does Not Exist.* The Coev. Quart. Sum.

Marx, K., Engels, F. 1976. *Sochineniya.* [Essays]. v.20, p.610. Moscow.

Menn, A. 1991.*Radostnaya Vest.* [Good News]. Moscow. (in Russian)

Moody, Raymond A. 1976. *Life after Life.* Bantam Books.

Moody, Raymond A. 1983. *Reflections on Life after Life.* Bantam Books.

Moody, Raymond A. 1992. *Zhizn Posle Smerti.* [Life After Life]. Moscow. (Russian translation)

Osis; Haraldson. 1976. *At the Hour of Death.* N.Y.

Pogorelski, M., 1899. *Elektrofotosfeny i Energografiya kak Dokazatelstvo Sushchestvovaniya Fiziologhicheskoi Polyarnoy Energhii.* [Electrophotosphens and Energography as proof of Physiological Polar Energy], St. Petersburg. (in Russian).

*Pravoslavnyi Sobesednik.* [Christian Correspondent], 1858, p.1, p.417. St. Petersburg. (in Russian).

Rahk, I.V. 1993.*Mify Dravnego Yeghipta.* [The Myths of Ancient Egypt]. (in Russian)

Rawlings, Maurice. 1980. *Before Death Comes.* London.

Rose, Seraphim, Hieromonk 1980. *The Soul After Death.* St.Herman of Alaska Br.

Rose, Seraphim, Hieromonk, 1991. *Dusha Posle Smerti.* [Soul After Death]. Moscow. (in Russian)

Rozanov, V.V. 1990.*Nesovmestimye Kontrasty Zhizni.* [Incompatible Contrasts of Life]. Moscow. (in Russian)

Sabom, Michael B.Dr. 1982. *Recollections of death.* Corgi books.

Satprem. 1989. *Sri Aurobindo.* Leningrad, LGU.

Steiner, R., 1991.*Ocherk Tainovedeniya.* [Essay on Mysticism]. Leningrad. (in Russian)

The Tibetan Book of the Dead. 1960. Oxford. NY.

*Tibetskaya Kniga Mertvykh.*, 1993. [The Tibetan Book of the Dead] Moscow. (Russian translation)

Tokarchik, A. 1992.*Mify o Bessmertii.* [Myths of Immortality]. Moscow. (in Russian)

*Vechnyia Zagrobnyia Tainy.* [Eternal Mysteries of After-Life]. 1992. (in Russian)

Voino-Yasenetskiy (Archbishop Luka), 1978.*Dukh. Dusha i Telo.* [Spirit. Soul and Body]. Zhizn s Bogom. (in Russian)

Waltari, Mika. 1993. *The Egyptian.* Helsinki.

Wilber, K. 1982. *The Holographic Paradigm and Other Paradoxes: Exploring the Leading Edge of Science.* Boulder, CO: Shambala.

Woodroffe, Sir John. 1960. The Science of Death in *The Tibetian Book of the Dead.* Oxford. NY.

Akimov, A.E.; Moskovskii, A.V. 1992. *Kvantovaya Nelokal'nost i Torsionnyie Polya* [Quantum non-locality and torsion fields]. Moscow, MNTTs "Vent" (in Russian).

Barrow, J.D.—Tipler, F.J. 1986, *The Anthropic Cosmological Priciple.* Oxford, Clarendon Press.

Bohm,1980; *Wholeness and the implicate order.* N.Y. Routledge & Co.

Burr H.S. 1972. *Blueprint for Immortality: The Electric Pattern of Life.* Neville Spearman.

Chizhevskii, A.L. 1976. *Zemnoye Ekho Solnechnykh Bur'* [Earthly echo of solar storms]. Moscow, Mysl' (in Russian).

De Sabbata V., Sivaram C. *Fifth Force as Manifestation of Torsion.* // Inter. J. Theor. Phys. 1990, N 1, p.1.

Dvoirin, G.B. 1992. *Yavleniye Predvaritel'novo Svetovovo Interferentsionnovo-Kodiruyushchevo Predstavlenyia Zritel'noi Informatsii v Opticheskom Prostranstve Setchatki Zhivovo Glaza* [Preliminary light-oriented interferential-coding transfer of visual information in the optical space of the living eye retina]. Uspekhi Fisiologicheskikh Nauk, v.23, #1, p121-125. Dep. in VINITI 04/15/87, #2605-V87 (in Russian).

Ereveyev, V.E. 1992. *Chertyozh Antropokosmosa* [Blueprint of anthropocosmos]. Moscow, ASM (in Russian).

Griffiths Bede. 1992. *A New Vision of Reality.* Fount Paperbacks.

Gurevich, A.G. 1944. *Teoriya Biologicheskovo Polya* [Theory of the biological field]. Moscow, GosIsdat (in Russian).

Gurwitsch A. 1922. *Ueber den Begriff des embrionalen Feldes.* Archiv fr Entwicklungsmechanik 51:383-415 (in German).

Hehl F.W. *On the Kinematics of the Torsion Space-Time.*// Found. Phys., 1985, v. 15, N 4, p. 451.

Hehl F.W.,Heyde P.,Kerlick G.D.,Nester J.M. *General relativity with spin and torsion.*// Rev. Mod. Phys., 1976, N 3, p. 393.

Jahn R., Dunne B. 1988. *Margins of Reality.* A Harvest/HBJ Book

Kazhinskii, B.B. 1963. *Biologicheskaya Radiosvyaz* [Biological radio communication]. Kiev (in Russian).

Kaznacheev, V.P.; Mikhailova, L.P. 1981. *Sverkhslabyie Izlucheniya v Mezhkletochnykh Vzaimodeistviyakh* [Superweak emissions in inter-cell interactions]. Novosibirsk, Nauka (in Russian).

Kaznacheev, V.P.; Mikhailova, L.P. 1985. *Bioinformatsionnaya Funtsiya Yestestvennykh Elektromagnitnykh Polei* [Bioinformational function of natural electromagnetic fields]. Novosibirsk, Nauka (in Russian).

Kaznacheev, V.P.; Spirin, E.A.1991. *Kosmoplanetarnyi Fenomen Cheloveka* [Cosmoplanetary phenomenon of man]. Novosibirsk, Nauka (in Russian).

Kniazeva, E.N; Kurdyumov, S.P. 1994.*Zakony Evolutsii i Samoorganizatsii Slozhnykh Sistem* [The laws of evolution and self-organization of complicated systems]. Moscow, Nauka (in Russian).

Kopczynski W. *A non-singular universe with torsion.* // Phys. Lett. A, 1972, N 39, p. 219.; Phys. Lett. A, 1973, N43, p.63.

Korotkov, K.G. 1995. *Effekt Kirlian* [Kirlian effect]. St. Petersburg (in Russian).

Kozyrev, N.A. 1982. *Vremya Kak Fizicheskoye Yavleniye* [Time as a physical phenomenon]. Riga.

Pribram . 1981. *The brain*// Millenium. Los-Angeles. J.I.Tarcher Inc.

Prigogine, I.; Stingers, I. 1986. *Poryadook iz Khaosa* [From chaos to order]. Moscow, Progres (in Russian).

Prigogine, I.; Stingers, I. 1994. *Vremya, Khaos, Kvant* [Time, chaos, quantum]. Moscow, Progres (in Russian).

Sheldrake Rupert. 1989. *The Presence of the Past.* Fontana. Collins

Shipov, G.I. 1992. *Teoriya Fizicheskovo Vakuuma* [Theory of physical vacuum]. Moscow, MNTTs "Vent" (in Russian).

Spemann H.C. 1938. *Embryonic Development and Induction. New Haven.* Yale University Press.

Suchonos, S. 1981. *Vzglyad Izdali* [A look from afar]. Znaniye-Sila #7, p32 (in Russian).

Vernadskii, V.I. 1989. *Biosfera i Noosfera.* Moscow, Nauka (in Russian).

Weiss P. 1939. *Principles of Development.* New York: Holt.

Wilber Ken (ed.) 1982. *The Holographic Universe and Other Paradoxes*, Shambhala, Boulder.

Wilber Ken (ed.) 1984. *Quantum Questions.* Shambhala, Boulder.

# INDEX

# Kirlian effect diagnostic chart

Name. . . . . . . . . . . . . . . . . . . . . . . . . . . . . Date . . . . . . . . . . . .

Stress level:    0    2    4    6    8    10

Deficiency ← —————— → Excess

| | 1 | 2 | 3 | 4 | 5 | 6 | 7 | 8 | 9 | 10 | Special attention |
|---|---|---|---|---|---|---|---|---|---|---|---|
| Cervical spine | | | | | | | | | | | |
| Thoracic spine | | | | | | | | | | | |
| Lumbar spine | | | | | | | | | | | |
| Sacral | | | | | | | | | | | |
| Coccyx | | | | | | | | | | | |
| **Cerebral zone** | | | | | | | | | | | |
| Eyes | | | | | | | | | | | |
| Ears | | | | | | | | | | | |
| Nose, frontal sinus | | | | | | | | | | | |
| Jaws | | | | | | | | | | | |
| Throat, tonsils, trachea | | | | | | | | | | | |
| **Blood circulation** | | | | | | | | | | | |
| Coronary vessels | | | | | | | | | | | |
| Heart | | | | | | | | | | | |
| **Lymph** | | | | | | | | | | | |
| **Abdominal zone** | | | | | | | | | | | |
| Duodenum | | | | | | | | | | | |
| Jejunum | | | | | | | | | | | |
| Ascending colon | | | | | | | | | | | |
| Transcerse colon | | | | | | | | | | | |
| Descending colon | | | | | | | | | | | |
| Sigmoid colon | | | | | | | | | | | |
| Appendix | | | | | | | | | | | |
| **Kidney** | | | | | | | | | | | |
| **Urinary system** | | | | | | | | | | | |
| **Liver** | | | | | | | | | | | |
| **Spleen** | | | | | | | | | | | |
| **Endocrine system** | | | | | | | | | | | |
| Thyroid gland | | | | | | | | | | | |
| **Thorax zone** | | | | | | | | | | | |
| Mammary glands | | | | | | | | | | | |
| Respiratory system | | | | | | | | | | | |
| **Reproductive area** | | | | | | | | | | | |